## "How you must despise me!"

Suddenly Wilda's face contorted and tears welled up before she could fight them off. The deep blue of her eyes trembled through the tears.

"How prettily you cry," Damien mocked. "God, yes, you're lovely! You have all the armory that makes men defenseless, but I'm onto you, little one, and it will be an immeasurable pleasure to disarm you the next time we find ourselves locked in combat."

"T–there won't be a next time," she flung at him. "I'm leaving Moonside. I can't bear the way you twist everything so I'm always in the wrong. You said that unbearable thing to me even as you m–made love to me—" Wilda couldn't go on.

"What's so terrible about the truth?" he asked. "No virgin was ever that responsive in a man's arms...."

VIOLET WINSPEAR
is also the author of these

# Harlequin Presents

and these

# Harlequin Romances

Many of these titles are available at your local bookseller.

For a free catalogue listing all available Harlequin Romances
and Harlequin Presents, send your name and address to:

HARLEQUIN READER SERVICE
1440 South Priest Drive, Tempe, AZ 85281
Canadian address: Stratford, Ontario N5A 6W2

# VIOLET WINSPEAR

## the love battle

*Harlequin Books*

TORONTO • LONDON • LOS ANGELES • AMSTERDAM
SYDNEY • HAMBURG • PARIS • STOCKHOLM • ATHENS • TOKYO

Harlequin Presents edition published February 1978
ISBN 0-373-10226-7

Second printing May 1980
Third printing July 1981

Original hardcover edition published in 1977
by Mills & Boon Limited

# CHAPTER ONE

WILDA stood very still in the shafting coolness of the ceiling fan, letting it play over her skin and hair. This part of the day always came as a welcome relief, when her employer was bedded down and she could feel free to relax until it was time to eat her solitary dinner in the *zala*.

All day Charmides had been as difficult as possible, impatient with the heat and the nagging pain in her back. She wasn't a woman who cared how much she kept the hired help on the run, and the day had been a sultry one, in keeping with the temperature on the Florida Keys at this time of the year. There had been that letter at breakfast, which Charmides had consulted at intervals throughout the day. She hadn't confided in Wilda, who as a sort of maid-companion was let in on all sorts of body secrets while being kept out of domestic ones. Charmides had sons and the writing on the envelope had been slashing and definite and darkly defined. Wilda was inclined to think that one of those sons had been in touch with his mother and had written something which had made Charmides irritable with everyone around her, especially her young maid of all work.

Not that Wilda was in any way the usual sort of skivvy. The very fact that she was an attractive young woman was enough to arouse speculation as to why she chose such an occupation when she could easily have found more congenial employment. The answer was that she liked the Florida Keys, liked this big Greek-built house above the beach in sound of the sea, and the solitary air of the place which stood in many acres of private ground.

She gave a yawn and a stretch of her lissom body. It was nice to be peaceful for a while and with a little smile she ruffled her fair hair, which fell back from her brow in a deep natural wave. She had a slender face set with dark blue eyes with a hint of purple in them ... witch of the wood eyes, her father had always called them. Her mouth had a natural flush to it, as if she had been biting into wild berries, and her skin was deep honey from the Florida sunshine.

Perhaps even a beautiful girl, for her iris eyes had a refulgent quality to them; a deep glow that was almost a storm light. The eyes of a girl who had some reason for distrusting anyone who tried to get inside her defences. These had been erected for some time now, ever since she had come to Moonside to wear the fawn linen uniform that Charmides insisted upon, perhaps to tone down her attractiveness and to keep her subjected. Wilda made no objection; she even seemed to welcome the anonymity which the uniform gave her, turning her into a member of the household staff whom visitors barely looked at.

This evening as usual Wilda was going to the beach for her dip in the cool ocean before the tide came rolling in, until the combers were huge silken scrolls in the starlight.

Her sandals whispered on the stairs as she ran down lightly, passing at intervals the arresting portraits of Charmides in real gold frames. A member of an old coast family of infinite breeding and a dash of ancient piracy, she had been a beauty and her husband, Greek–

American shipping magnate Helios Demonides, had been tremendously proud of her ... though their marriage had never been an idyllic one. He had too often been occupied with his shipping concerns to give her the attention she demanded, so instead he had given her a couple of sons. Damien was the elder by two years, his brother Troy the father's favourite who had followed him into the business.

Wilda suspected that Damien was the thorn in his mother's side, for though she spoke often of Troy and was obviously proud of him, she rarely mentioned her eldest son. She didn't even keep a photograph of him at her bedside; in the twin silver frames there was a picture of her dark-browed husband, who had died a decade ago, and the younger son who resembled his mother rather than the commanding Greek who had been her husband.

Damien Demonides was a kind of freewheeling financial consultant, whom the managements of large corporations employed to advise on their financial investments ... he was, in more earthy terms, a very shrewd gambler with an instinct for playing the stock market like a roulette wheel, more often placing the ball on the winning number than the losing one. That his mother had passed on to him the old piratical family trait was probably at the root of her dissatisfaction with him, and Wilda couldn't be a member of the Moonside household staff without having heard that Damien was a wild one who had never taken readily to the Greek father's dictums, or the mother's natural desire to have from her sons the doting affection that the ever-busy Helios denied her. This house had seen many a domestic storm, Wilda reckoned, but she had grown intensely fond of the place.

Wilda came out upon the steps that led down to the private beach fronting the Villa Moonside. She breathed the scent of sweet by night overlaid by the tang of the ocean. The daytime sultriness had given way to coolness and beauty, and Wilda loved the solitude and the surf crooning upon the shoreline rocks. Right now she wouldn't have exchanged places with a movie star or a princess. She didn't mind being a maid-companion when she had all this loveliness thrown in.

An evening as still and sensuous as dark velvet, with the golden claw marks of stars across the silent sky ... Wilda was halfway across the creamy sands when she came to a sudden halt and stared downwards at a folded pile of masculine clothing on the beach. She stared in amazement at a cream denim jacket, brown slacks and a lighter brown shirt of corded silk. Atop the pile were silk socks, a jock-strap and a pair of camel suede casuals.

Strangers weren't allowed to trespass on this beach, even ones who wore stylish and costly clothes. She glanced up with a frown, her fingers clenching hard on the bathing-suit and beach towel which she carried. A tall figure was wading out of the sea, water streaming from his lean and powerful body. He was like some pagan sea-god, sun-coppered, hard and picturesque. Tangled in the thick wet hair of his chest was the chain of a golden medal, and Wilda stood there petrified as he came directly towards where she stood beside his clothes ... she wanted to run and yet was incapable of movement.

He looked right at her, he obviously saw that she was a young woman, but his flexible stride didn't falter for a second and he continued towards her, a flagrant, confident, unashamed masculinity about him that left her breathless. It wasn't so much that she had never seen a naked man before—it was simply that she had never seen one who was so casual about it. He was probably aware that he had a fine body, but he made no concession at all to her possible modesty ... added to which was the disquieting awareness that she had seen him before, and in circumstances that made her heart miss a beat.

The moment she looked at his face Wilda remembered him ... that strong-featured face stamped with self-will, blood pride, charm and a tinge of cruelty. That pagan quality was unforgettable, along with those saturnine brows above grey eyes that smoked, that mocked, that didn't give a damn if he was liked or detested.

Wilda hadn't known his name, but she had seen him in the restaurant of the Hotel St Cyr where she had played the guitar and sung her plaintive songs. He had been staying in a suite along the hall, that night Myles Sadlier's wife had proclaimed to Monte Carlo at large that she had just found her husband in bed with a 'little blonde slut'.

Nerves jangled in Wilda's body and that old fear of discovery was alive in her veins again. Her dark blue eyes clung to this man's and she silently begged him not to remember her as the *chanteuse* in that hotel, from which she had fled away nearly two years ago ... that silly little innocent who had been given knockout drops in her tomato juice, and had awakened in the bedroom of Myles Sadlier—with his wife there, screaming that she had caught them *in flagrante delicto*. Wilda, a girl alone, without any defence against the fact that she was young and fair and creamy-skinned, had been cited in the divorce despite the fact that nothing intimate had happened in that hotel room. Myles had wanted to be free of his wife, and he had paid Wilda some flattering attention in the way of an older man, and when she wouldn't really sleep with him, had resorted to a trick often used in the Hollywood films he produced. It had worked. The young *chanteuse* with no protector had been used by a hard sophisticate for his purpose ... that he hadn't actually touched her was still a mystery to Wilda. She could only suppose that Sadlier, knowing her to be a virginal girl, had developed cold feet and been scared of a possible rape charge.

All the same it had been a cheap and degrading experience, for who would believe that she was an inexperienced girl when French newspapers had carried details of the scandalous *affaire* of the British singer caught in bed with a famous producer of films, his wife suing for her divorce on grounds of gross misconduct on the part of her husband.

Wilda inwardly groaned, for only a short while ago the beach at Moonside had seemed like paradise. Now she dropped her gaze to the silky hardness of this intruder's shoulders and felt as if Satan had come into the peaceful garden.

In the shifting light of the stars his face seemed dangerous, and then with a thrust of his hand he pushed the wet hair back from his strong brow. 'The water's like silk if you're going in,' he said, and his voice carried the slight rasp of someone who smoked rather a lot. He bent casually to the pile of clothes and picked up the jock-strap. 'If you aren't going in, then perhaps you'd be a good girl and turn your back for a minute or two.'

Wilda held her breath, and then released it. 'You're intruding here—this is private property!' she gasped.

'I'm well aware of that,' and as he spoke he put his free hand against her shoulder and spun her away from him, so she was facing the other way. 'I always think that nudity only gets indecent when we have to start covering it—don't you?'

'You could get into trouble,' Wilda informed him, a wild flush of colour in her cheeks, and a wilder hope in her heart that in the two years that had passed this man had forgotten the night when he had strolled from the hotel lift only to come about a scene straight out of French farce, with an infuriated wife dragging from her husband's bedroom a young girl with fair flowing hair and a frightened face.

'I rather flourish on trouble,' he drawled, and she caught the rasp of a zip and the electrical slither of silk over bare skin. 'You can turn round, honey, if you've quite recovered from the shock of seeing me.'

'W-what do you mean?' She swung round, fear quickening her pulsebeat.

'You did rather look at me as if you hadn't known that boys are just a little different from girls.' The edge of his mouth gave a wanton quirk as he flicked open a pack of Lambert and Butler Internationals and offered them.

'No, thanks, I don't smoke.' Wilda eyed him suspiciously and couldn't help noticing that his untamed look had changed subtly into a dark if rather wicked distinction. As he slid one of the long cigarettes between his lips, he was also running his smoke-grey eyes over her, taking in her hair as it tumbled carelessly to the shoulders of her uniform. Throughout the day Wilda wore a nape knot, but each evening she released

11

her hair so she could feel the sea breezes right through to her scalp, her ears, the smooth skin of her throat. Right now she felt rather like a cat on a shaky ledge, for she wasn't certain who this man was who came invading the Demonides' beach. She only knew that he had been a witness two years ago to her mortification at the Hotel St Cyr, and his eyes refused to confirm or deny that he recognised her. The uniform could be off-putting, she thought hopefully, for its sedate neatness was very unlike the costume he had seen her in the last time they had come face to face.

Then she had been wearing the purple silk jacket of Myles Sadlier's pyjamas, which that infamous man had put her into while she lay drugged. The jacket had covered her to her thighs, leaving her legs long and bare and somehow very erotic in contrast to the purple silk. With her unbound hair and eyes still dazed and large-pupilled from the effect of the knockout drops, she could only have looked what Sadlier's wife had called her, and Wilda felt her skin flaming here in the night air of the beach filled with salty spray.

'A girl of all the virtues, eh?' The stranger cupped his hand to shield his lighter flame from the breeze blowing up the beach now that the tide was turning the sea. The irony in his deep, slightly rasping voice wasn't lost on Wilda, and she felt an agony of doubt and confusion. Had he remembered her, or was this his usual mode of address to a girl?

'You've had your swim,' she said with an attempt at cool dignity. 'Now you'd better be on your way, for as I told you before this beach is privately owned and my employer doesn't like intruders.'

'Your employer?' he murmured. 'Madame Charmides, eh, who lives in the sun temple on the incline?'

He gestured with his cigarette. 'So you're her maid, are you, who at the end of the day comes running into the arms of Neptune? Now the tide's rolling in and those combers get bigger all the time, so best abandon your sport with the sea king for this evening. You don't want to get battered to bits on those rocks.'

Wilda stared at him, watching the smoke curl up against his sun-dark skin. He seemed to know about this beach, and she grew suddenly afraid that he might be a friend of the family—if he recognised her as the girl in the Sadlier divorce case, then he could lose her this job at Moonside if he mentioned the fact to Charmides. If there was one thing Wilda had learned during the months of her employment here, it was that her employer had an obsession about honesty. As a very rich woman she insisted on servants with impeccable references, and Wilda had asked a friend from her college days to write a reference for her; a girl who had married into the Chaim-Freeman banking family in Boston, who had regarded the request as a bit of a prank. But as Mrs Chaim-Freeman the fourth she could write a reference and not have it disputed, and this highly flattering letter, along with several months' experience as a nurse-aide in a private clinic, had served to get Wilda the job she now had—and she didn't want to lose it.

She had found a niche for herself which excluded contact with people like the Sadliers—but now the ground seemed to be shaking under her feet. A stranger from the past had appeared out of the night, and there was about him the look of a man who could be charming or cruel as the mood took him.

'Do you mind if I ask who you are?' she asked suddenly, taking the bull by the horns.

'Not at all, girl with the virginal blue eyes.' Smoke clouded about his smoky grey eyes so they narrowed into a slightly menacing glitter between black lashes. 'My name is Damien, and though I doubt if my dear Mamoushka often mentions me, I am sure you have heard the name. Again in the old tradition the prodigal son returns, except that I don't return with my portion spent and my clothes in tatters. Ah, the way you look at me with those eyes! The colour of the iris—most unusual—quite unforgettable.'

Wilda swayed, and the next instant felt hard fingers gripping her wrist. 'You need your dinner,' he said. 'No doubt you've been on your feet since early morning, attending to the wants of my lovely but most demanding mother. Come, shall we go in? Distant traces of boyhood in me are clamouring a little to see if the house is still the same.'

Right through to her bones Wilda seemed to feel that grip of warm sure fingers, and though she wanted to shake free of him, quite certain he had recognised her and was playing cat and mouse with her, she obeyed an instinct which warned her not to let him see that she was unnerved by his manner.

They walked from the beach towards the steps that led indoors and she could feel him running his eyes over the arcaded white and red-roofed house with its gracefully curving wings. The walls were cobbled and had bunches of rock plants trailing from the grooves. A terrace led up from one side to a balustrade hanging sheer above the beach, and here and there were stone walkways and little flights of steps. To look at Moonside was to be transported to some Grecian island ... it was the most attractive place Wilda had ever seen, and sudden curiosity made her glance at Damien

Demonides to see how he was reacting to the house in which he had been born.

His black brows were drawn into a single line, and Wilda thought of the saying that if a man's eyebrows met in the middle there was no way for the devil to be let out of his mind.

'My father never lost his desire for Greece,' he murmured. 'It's there in the house he built, and it was always in the way he treated me. The firstborn son has to be a paragon of all the virtues, even if they have to be whipped in. I merely wanted to be Damien, myself, not some image of another man. You see that terrace up there? On my sixteenth birthday he and I had some argument—I believe it was over my youthful addiction to ice-hockey and the fact that I was neglecting school studies to stay on the hockey team—and in a sudden Spartan rage he swung his hand at me and nearly sent me head over heels over that balustrade. He grabbed hold of me, and then had the nerve to hit me again for making him lose his Greek dignity. If he wanted me to be Greek he should have sent me to Athens to study, but he wanted it both ways. He wanted an American education for me, but he couldn't accept the freedom of spirit that went with it, the ability to feel affection for one's family without being tied to the father's belt and the mother's cord. In Greece a son never stops being the shadow of his *patir*, and a daughter never ceases to be dominated by her mother. They call it love, but children should always be like birds, free to take flight when they're ready to spread their wings. I had to fly away without the blessing of my parents, and they never forgave me for it.'

He paused and the slant to his eyebrows made him look entirely sardonic. 'They gave me no portion to

15

spend, but it didn't matter. I had my wits and I knew how to use them. When it came to Troy my father made no second mistake, as he regarded it. My brother studied in Greece and he took the reins of the shipping firm when Helios fell ill and lost his strength. I admire Troy, but I sometimes wonder if he ever had a fraction of the fun I have managed to slice in between the earning of my bread—what is life without a little madness? *Moussaka* without the aubergine!'

The grey eyes flashed downwards and captured Wilda's gaze. 'I daresay you could vouch for that, eh?'

Wilda caught her breath and felt the hot colour sweep over her cheekbones, rising to her brow and burning into the roots of her hair. In that moment she knew he hadn't forgotten a detail of that bedroom scene at the Hotel St Cyr. His mind was too keen and well-trained for him to forget a single detail of any occurrence in his life, and that flicker of sheer wickedness in his eyes told her that he took her for what everyone had called her ... Myles Sadlier's little piece of fun who had been caught out with him in a flagrant affair and dragged on display by his infuriated wife.

That mortifying incident in Wilda's life felt right now as if it were being repeated ... she had hoped and prayed that the past was behind her, but instead it was right here beside her in the shape of Charmides' son, and there was something about him that told Wilda he could be quite ruthless in his pursuit of a business deal ... or a woman, and he was looking at her as if he might find it diverting to pick up where he obviously thought Myles Sadlier had left off.

'Would you mind letting go of my wrist,' Wilda said tensely.

'I don't know that I want to let go of it.' He raised

her hand and studied her slim fingers that wore no rings, and her fine-boned wrist that carried a little porcelain heart on a chunky gold chain.

'Is this little thing,' he prodded the heart with a fingertip, 'indicative of your heart, *pedhi mou*?' And with his fingers tightening about her wrist so the chain pressed the bone he ran his eye over her tapering cheekbones, her startled mouth, and lissom figure in the neat uniform. 'How the devil do you come to be working for my mother—as a maid?'

'I—I'm more of a companion. I've been here nearly a year and I like working here——' Wilda spoke defensively, for he had the power to have her thrown out of Moonside this very night; that awareness was like a sword suspended between them, shining and sharp. This house on the edge of the sea had become like a home to Wilda ... there was just nowhere else to go, except to a women's hostel. Her home in England had long been broken up when her beloved father had died and her mother had married a Frenchman and gone to Provence to live. She had been in tune with her father, who had composed light music for films and television, and who had taught her how to sing and play both the guitar and the piano. That was how she had earned a living before that traumatic business at Monte Carlo, but she had never really liked the life and could no longer go back to it.

She gazed at Damien Demonides and knew that his denial of his basic Greek nature was based on his awareness that he was fundamentally far more Greek than American. It was inborn in him to respect only women of modesty and restraint, and he had the so-called evidence of his own eyes and the much-reported facts of the Sadlier divorce case to confirm that she, his

17

mother's maid-companion, was not a girl to respect. The hard set to his jaw made her heart beat like a drum, added to which she could feel the porcelain heart bruising her flesh beneath the pressure of his hard fingers.

'What did you do about a reference?' he asked insolently. 'Forge one in order to bluff your way into Moonside? I know my mother and she's a difficult woman to fool. You must be quite the actress as well as a singer of plaintive melodies *à la pierrot*.'

Wilda felt the shock-wave of actually hearing him admit that he knew her ... it left her reeling inside, yet she had to fight back; had to erase that insolent look from his eyes.

'You aren't going to get any kicks out of tormenting me,' she said fiercely. 'Go and tell your mother right now that I'm the notorious Wilda Bird who sang for her supper! It's true, she has never connected me with scandal because that was only a stage name. I've worked hard for madame, and she knows me as Wilda Grayson, my real name, but if you're going to expose me to her bit by painful bit, then I'd sooner get it over with to-night. I'm no mouse to be played about with by you or anyone else!'

'How true,' he drawled. 'No mouse ever had eyes like yours, or such a wanton wave to hair like a silky skein of gold. What a pity it's all on the outside, that look of sweet warm candour and grace. I guess that's how my mother got taken in, eh? She accepted the wrapping for the contents?'

'Damn you!' Wilda stormed. 'Why did you have to come home to Moonside? Even your own mother has no time for you!'

'True again,' he admitted, looking quite unconcerned by Wilda's outburst. 'You and I would appear to be a pair of black sheep—though in your case the pelt is more like Jason's golden fleece. So you imagine I'm going to take the shears to you and expose you piece by delectable piece, eh? You don't know me, *melle mou*.'

'I'm not your honey,' she rejoined. 'And I don't intend to be, if that's what you're hinting. You don't blackmail me, *kyrie!*'

'Blackmail you?' He quirked an eyebrow and his eyes were deeply amused in the slanting light of the lamp attached to the wall of the big porch. 'My dear girl, I probably earn in one hour what you are paid for a week's work.'

'Y-you know what I mean.' Wilda flung back her hair and regarded him with resentful eyes. 'It's in the tradition, isn't it, the poor maid at the mercy of the son of the house? I'll walk all the way to the railway station rather than stay here to endure that—from you!'

'What an imagination, and how the eyes glow like storm signals.' His smile was infinitely mocking. 'You should have gone to Hollywood, where any kind of notoriety is the pass key to fame and fortune. Whatever induced a beauty like you to take on maid's work? Are you trying to inveigle your way into my mother's last will and testament?'

That did it! In a sudden release of torment, repressed in her ever since Monto Carlo, Wilda swung her free hand at Damien's face and landed a blow right against his dominant Greek nose. He winced as the pain shot through the tissues of his nose, and the next instant he let go of her and swiftly pulled a handkerchief from his pocket. Wilda stared in a kind of horrified fascination as the white linen became

19

spattered with bright drops of blood.

He held the handkerchief to his nose, exerting pressure, while he gazed at Wilda with quizzical eyes. 'That's quite a left hook you have. No one's given me a bloody nose since my schooldays.'

'Something else for you to tell your mother,' she said coldly. 'But tell me something, don't Greeks ever forget and forgive?'

'It's according to what they have to—forgive,' he halted on that word and a rather odd expression came into his grey eyes. 'For what it's worth, I have no intention of giving you away to Charmides. She hired you and it's for her to fire you. Almost a year at Moonside, eh? You must have quite a lot of staying power, as my dear mother isn't one of the easiest of women to get along with. As an employer she must be hell in peach silk and perfume!'

'We get along all right.' Wilda bit her lip. 'Has your nose stopped bleeding?'

'Just about, but don't spoil the Bette Davis scene by going all female. You thoroughly enjoyed landing me that wallop and you know it.'

'I did,' she admitted, but deep down she felt a twinge of shame. She hadn't been brought up to be a shrew who fought with a man, but it frightened her, the way Damien Demonides had come here out of the night and suddenly brought with him memories of a time and a place she wanted to forget. That she had been entirely innocent was quite beyond proving ... she had been in Sadlier's bedroom half-naked, and this man had seen her thrown out of that room wearing only a masculine pyjama jacket. If she said to him here and now: 'I was drugged by that beast of a man. He wanted a divorce and he used me to get it,' this hard-

20

featured, sardonic Greek would only look scornful. Because he was a Greek in his bones and blood he regarded women as having two main functions in life, to be good wives and mothers. Any women outside the domestic sphere had another purpose, and that was to provide pleasure. In Damien's eyes she came into the last category, and suddenly it troubled Wilda and hurt deep down inside her that she should see her in that sensual light.

If he didn't mean to reveal her past to Charmides, then what did he intend to do?

'Will you be staying at Moonside?' she asked suddenly, remembering the letter which Charmides had received and frowned over.

'Yes—have you any objection, young woman?' He folded his handkerchief so the bloodstains were concealed. 'Did *manoula mou* throw a tantrum when she opened my letter to say I was coming home for a few weeks? Did she throw all her scent bottles and potions through the window?'

'Your mother said nothing at all to me about your possible arrival, which is why I was so—so startled when I saw you in the water.'

'Coming out of the water,' he drawled, that wicked gleam back in his eyes. 'Like Daemon, eh? Terror of the night? It must have come as quite a shock to see someone who might recognise you as lovelorn pierrot.'

'I was never lovelorn,' she gasped.

'Then all the worse, my child. Love can sometimes excuse a couple from a mad fling in a hotel bedroom, but to admit you weren't in love! Shameless hussy!'

'Oh, think what you must!' Wilda turned to the door and pushed it open, and there in the hall was a pile of Louis Vuitton luggage with leather handles and that tailored look, and atop the cases a car coat lined with llama wool. His belongings had been brought in from the entrance that faced the road, where no doubt a sleek, custom-made car was parked.

He followed her into the hall, carrying the bathing-suit and beach towel which had dropped from her hand when she hit him.

Here the lights were full on and when he handed Wilda her bathing gear she saw him in alarming detail. The lean and confident body in tailored clothing. A sardonic knowledge of the world deep in his eyes ... a man who made everything seem more alive, more vital with meaning. He ran a finger across the bridge of his nose and he gave a laugh so low in his throat it was barely audible.

Wilda had never heard anyone laugh like that, as if there smouldered in him a promise of vengeance for the painful blow she had landed on that bold feature of his face ... an utterly Greek face, with hair still rough from the sea and like the pelt of a black ram!

Her heart crested a wave of panic ... a confrontation with Charmides was going to be avoided, but at what sort of a cost? She wasn't, as Damien Demonides believed, an experienced girl of the world who went after other women's husbands; she was a girl of twenty-two who had never been in love or indulged in any kind of exploration of the senses. She had enjoyed the intelligence and charm of her father too much to welcome the fumbling attentions of young men ... yet here she was, a maid at Moonside with the son of the house looking at her in a way she had never experienced in her life.

The pupils of his eyes were so expanded that they

blotted out the grey irises and Wilda felt trapped in pools of burning darkness.

Trapped was the only word that applied to the feeling she felt when Damien looked at her, that strain of corsair in his blood letting a devil into his eyes.

He leaned a little closer to her and said, softly: 'Suspense, *melle mou*, is one of the most enjoyable sensations our flesh is heir to.'

'And what do you mean by that?' She retreated a step and he followed, still bringing with him that wicked glint in his eyes.

'I'm not a snitch, Wilda Bird, so your secret is safe with me, but if you stay on at Moonside you'll be sticking your pretty neck out.'

'Will I?' Wilda had a curious sensation, as if she might lose her breath at any moment. 'You mean— you'll take advantage of my position here?'

'Why not? I came home expecting a less than exciting vacation on the Keys and I find at Moonside a pretty, blue-eyed husband-stealer playing at housemaid. The scenario writes itself, little one.'

'So you're threatening me, Mr Demonides? I either pack my bag and leave these premises, or you will try and seduce me? Is that how the script is written?'

'Exactly, if your sort of girl can be seduced?'

Wilda's eyes grew stormy and her cheeks wildly flushed, combining with the natural red of her shapely mouth to make her quite stunning as she stood there breathing quickly, hating every inch of Damien Demonides ... and he stood about six feet and three inches in his camel suede casuals.

'Go to the devil,' she said in her sweet clear English voice. 'You aren't going to frighten me away from a job I find entirely to my liking. You have a bold

Greek nose, *kyrie*, and I'll make it bleed again if you attempt to touch me against my will!'

So saying, Wilda turned and made for the staircase that spread like a polished fan across the hall, and behind her as she hurried away she heard Charmides' black ram of a son laughing softly to himself. About halfway up the stairs Wilda felt a compulsion to turn and give him one more glance, this devil who had strolled into the garden she had found for herself and whispered things that made her tingle with fury. Now he was lounging against the carved pillar that supported the handrail of the stairs, gazing up at her, eyebrows saturnine and densely black above his mocking eyes, as if fully aware that she would turn and look at him again.

Dark, smoky-eyed, and quite confident he could make a girl bend to his will any time he chose.

Wilda felt an urge to flee along the gallery as if the devil himself were in pursuit of her, but she restrained the impulse and gave a disdainful toss of her lovely hair. It fell about her eyes in those wanton waves, as he had called them, and quite distinctly she heard him softly whistling in perfect tune, *'When a bad, bad boy like me Meets a good, good girl like you.'*

Only he didn't believe she was a good, good girl!

## CHAPTER TWO

SPANGLES of sea light danced across the ceiling of Wilda's bedroom and she awoke gradually out of a sleep that had been a restless one, preceded by a tray

24

in her room because, for the very life of her, she couldn't have faced dinner in the *zala* in the company of Damien Demonides.

Wilda slipped from the bedcovers and entered the small pink-tiled bathroom which adjoined her room. She flung off her nightdress, pulled on a plastic cap and stepped beneath the invigorating tingle of the needle-spray shower, where she washed with foam gel, delighting in the scented freshness of her skin after she had rinsed off and dried herself. She put on cool lingerie and a freshly laundered uniform, and with deft hands twirled her hair into a nape knot and securely pinned it.

A glance in the chinoiserie wall-mirror assured her that all was neat and shining, the way Charmides liked her maid-companion to look. No make-up was permitted except for a light application of face powder, but as it happened Wilda was one of those English girls with a lovely skin through which a natural glow could be seen, and her eyes had no need of a cosmetic to intensify their deep blueness.

She took a look at her wristwatch and was relieved that she still had a few more minutes to herself, which she used in pacing her room in a rather troubled way. She had to formulate some plan of action with regard to Charmides' son ... what did she do, ignore him? Hopeless! That would be like standing in the middle of Manhattan and pretending the skyscrapers weren't there! No, she'd be terribly British and polite and try not to let him put a spark to the tinder of her temper.

Wilda paused and gripped the peacock-back of a canework chair and stared unseeingly at a lovely old Tiffany lamp on the little table beside the chair. Perhaps she should confide in Charmides and trust her employer to believe she had been the innocent victim of a heartless swine. So vulnerable at twenty years of age, still feeling deeply the loss of a much-loved father, and likely to fall prey to false sympathy from a middle-aged man.

Would Charmides listen to her? Was there any hope that the woman would emerge from her total self-absorption and feel the distress of someone other than herself?

Wilda doubted it. Charmides had been for too many years a woman of wealth who could indulge her own selfishness, and Wilda was merely someone she employed to keep her comfortable in her large and luxurious boudoir from which she rarely emerged. Apart from a back injury received some years ago in a fall, Charmides was in quite good health, but like many another rich and idle woman she believed she was in a precarious state of health and coddled herself outrageously. Champagne for a mid-morning pick-up was only one of her 'little vices' as she called them, and another was custom-made milk chocolates with no hard centres. And every so often a charming Hebrew came from New York and she bought from him lovely items of jewellery which she wore in bed.

No, thought Wilda, she would just have to take care to avoid Damien Demonides and hope he didn't mean to stay too long at Moonside. Bracing her shoulders, she left her room and went along the gallery in the direction of her employer's beautiful suite of rooms.

The morning was palmy with a sparkle to it, and in through open windows at either end of the gallery came the tangy aroma of eucalyptus trees from the gardens below, where the lovely jacarandas would be stretching their blue petals in the sun, and the yellow tangerines expanding their pores to release their delectable scent. A little later, when Wilda had got her mistress settled with her breakfast tray, she would go down to the walled garden and eat her own bacon and eggs beneath a pair of huge hibiscus trees, one pale pink and the other a mass of gorgeous rose flowers.

Quietly, making no sound on the thick cream carpet of Charmides' bedroom, Wilda entered and went over to the wide windows, where she pulled open the silk-lined curtains. In the big maplewood bed, with lambrequin posts that held a canopy of silver brocade, Charmides gave a protesting groan against the sudden invasion of sunlight.

'*Kalimera*, madame.' Wilda was studying Greek at Charmides' suggestion, and she enjoyed using the words she had so far mastered. 'It's a splendid morning and I do wish you'd come down and eat breakfast in the garden. The fresh air would do you so much good.'

'For heaven's sake, girl, don't talk to me about food and fresh air until I've got my face on! Quickly now!' Charmides struggled into a sitting position against the big embroidered pillows and tugged a sleeping cap from her tinted hair. Wilda went to the vanity-table and picked up the silver tray of lotions, oils and astringents, sensing from her employer's agitation that she knew of her son's arrival at the villa and expected him to come and see her at any moment.

The diamonds sparkled on her hands and the rubies glimmered as she removed night-cream with a tissue and proceeded with the aid of paint and powder to try and look as beautiful as the huge portrait of herself on the panelled wall facing the fourposter.

It was a hopeless task, of course. Self-indulgence had long since melted the firm-boned lines of the once lovely face, and there were wrinkles where once there had been flirtatious dimples. Charmides painted lipstick over the lips that had lost their youth, and Wilda could feel the painted eyes upon her, taking in her fresh, fair looks, and the glow that came through her clear skin.

'We have a house guest,' Charmides said, abruptly. 'You will be meeting him shortly, so I might as well tell you that it's my son Damien. I had his letter yesterday to say he might be coming, but I hoped he would change his mind. He and I both believe in speaking our minds, so inevitably we clash. I advise you to keep out of his way as much as possible. Your sort, my dear, are *hors-d'oeuvres* on the trolley as far as he's concerned.'

Wilda was quite sure of it, but she said composedly, 'You are aware by now, madame, that I don't play around, and I shall be extra discreet where your son is concerned. Are you pleased—at all—that he has come to see you?'

'To put it frankly, Wilda, I'm astonished. The last I heard of him he was at Zurs performing acrobatics on skis and persuading rich fools to invest in the companies he freelances for. He's a rake! Troy has the blood of his sober family!'

Wilda, recalling the hard but striking features of Damien's face, was inwardly in disagreement with that statement, but Charmides was unaware that he and Wilda had already met and it would be disastrous to mention how they had met!

'There!' The tray of cosmetics was handed to Wilda. 'How do I look now—no, don't tell me, for God's sake!' Charmides gave a theatrical shudder; an actress to her fingertips though she had never been on the stage. 'A woman's life is one continuation of torments. One's figure is so seductive at first—like yours—and then gradually it falls into ruin like an old house. And the face—there's nothing more tragic, believe me, than seeing your beauty fading away like a plucked flower until it's nothing more than a wrinkled mask! I'd like to smash every mirror in the world, do you know that?'

'You have your memories, madame,' Wilda said reasonably. 'I'm sure they've been good ones—you were very beautiful and your husband adored you. Everyone knows that.'

'Oh yes, he liked to have my portrait painted and he enjoyed seeing me in lovely gowns and jewels, but do you honestly suppose, you foolish child, that a woman prefers the pedestal to the bed? I had a tycoon for a husband and he preferred a board meeting any day, or night, to a love session. Greeks! They aren't the most attentive men in the world—though now and again Apollo gets born again, and Daphne, if she isn't a complete fool, stands still instead of running away. Bah, what am I talking about? It's having Damien here again, waking up the old wounds so that they ache again!'

'Do you want your breakfast now, madame?' Wilda asked, rather taken aback, but hoping she didn't show it, that Charmides had given way to such an intimate outburst. She usually enjoyed the legend that she had been the stunningly beautiful and adored wife of one of America's foremost shipping magnates, but there had been bitterness in her words just now ... a residue of acid in the Greek wine.

'No.' Charmides shook her head. 'I have no appetite just yet—he'll come and see me in a short while and I want you here when he does come, so you'll have to wait for your own breakfast.'

'As you wish, madame.' Wilda was disconcerted by the request and would have preferred to leave this room before Damien Demonides appeared in it. 'But don't you want to be alone with your son, especially if you haven't seen one another for some time?'

'It's been nearly two years.' Charmides sighed even as she frowned. 'He sends me gifts to mark Christmas or a birthday, but we have drifted apart and soon we shall be like strangers. As a boy—he was a remarkably nice boy, if you can believe it!'

Wilda didn't know what to believe ... she only knew that he was a remarkably disturbing man.

'You can do my hair for me,' Charmides said crisply. 'The upswept style that makes me look dignified.'

'Yes, madame.' Wilda proceeded to comb her employer's hair, lilac-tinted now that its glossy auburn had faded to grey. She fetched pins from the vanity-table and had just secured the final coil when fingers rapped the bedroom door ... and her heart seemed to repeat those raps.

The door swung open and Damien strolled into the luxuriously appointed room in which his look of audacious virility seemed intensified in contrast to silvery brocade and pink silk chairs and lounger.

Wilda tried not to look at him but her eyes had a will of their own; he was clad in tapered cream slacks and a tan shirt open against his equally tanned throat. The shirt had short sleeves and his arms were strong and dark-haired, the strap of his wrist-watch matching the narrow crocodile belt that clasped his trousers against his flat stomach. He had an aura of maleness that was more than a possession of muscles, and though his eyes flickered briefly in Wilda's direction, not a movement of his face revealed that he knew her.

'*Manoula mou!*' He strode to the bedside, encircled his mother with hard brown arms and laid kisses at either side of her face. 'You are looking well—dare I add that you have put on a little weight?'

'You'll dare, Damien, even if I hate you for saying it,' she rejoined. 'You are looking fit yourself. How have you been?'

'*Endaxi,*' he replied in Greek, and this time he glanced deliberately at Wilda, as if wondering why she remained in the room. 'Is your maid awaiting an order?' he drawled.

Charmides glanced at Wilda, hesitated a moment, and then said to him : 'This girl takes care of me and is in much of my confidence. She has been with me quite a time now and we get along—I informed Wilda that you had come home for a visit and she knows that my nerves are rather shaken up. I prefer her to stay, Damien. After all, we have nothing of an intimate nature to discuss. We grow more and more like strangers. You live your life, and leave me much alone to live mine, whereas Wilda is always here to keep me company.'

'Wilda,' he murmured, that gleam of impudence deep in his eyes as they dwelt on her slim figure near the windows where the sunlight came in and stroked her hair and the slim honey-cream of her neck. 'A most unusual name—I can only recall hearing it once before, but that was long ago and far away.'

Nerves twisted in the region of Wilda's midriff and she longed to retreat from Damien and the subtle game

31

he was playing with her, pretending to his mother that they were strangers and yet giving everything he said a double meaning. Her torment was subtle, as if she were a moth trapped by a flame; she wanted to dart away and yet was held by the silk drapes as if tranced.

'Well, Damien, your look of *zoikos* never grows less. In fact it increases with the years.' Charmides was looking her son over, from his thick black hair to his lean hips. 'No, you don't change, do you? How you racked my poor body when you were born, and Helios was highly delighted at that time. He carried you out on to the terrace and showed you to the moon. I cried out to him not to do it—that you'd be turned into a pagan, but he only laughed. The sun-god showing off his son to the moon-goddess.'

'And what are you looking for, *manoula mou*?' He lounged against one of the carved bedposts, a deep crevice of amusement in his cheek. 'The horns and the tail?'

'They're there, even if I can't see them,' she retorted. 'Hasn't the time yet come for you to follow Troy's example and become engaged to a nice girl?'

'One of the coastal aristocrats, dear mother? Or maybe a Bostonian heiress with too much blue blood and not enough red?'

'I want nice, well-reared girls for both my sons,' Charmides said arrogantly. 'No son of mine is going to throw himself away on less than the best.'

'What a snob you are!' he laughed softly.

'One of the blessings of a rich invalid, Damien, is that I can please myself and be bigoted if I choose. You please yourself! You always did!'

'I'm not a snob, dear one,' he drawled. 'So brother Troy has got himself a fiancée. A very nice girl, I take it, loaded with Vassar charm and lots of paternal dollars?'

'Oodles.' Charmides smiled, and Wilda saw her painted eyes roaming again the tall, lean figure at the side of her bed, little gleams of self-satisfaction in her eyes at having produced this intensely virile son from her own body. 'You have grown rich yourself, eh? You have the shrewd brains of your father and should have gone into the business when he asked you to do so. You could have taken some of the burdens from his shoulders and he might have lived a little longer.'

'Don't blame me for Patir's death.' Damien's grey eyes were suddenly dark with menace. 'He worked hard long hours by choice, all his life, and I had no interest in shipping.'

'No, you wanted to play with stocks and shares as a child plays with counting blocks!'

'Yes, it suits my temperament. I couldn't sit behind a desk and dictate orders to a bunch of sycophants who pretended loyalty to my face and planned mayhem behind my back. I heard that a clique of Father's so-called loyalists went to the Waldorf and drank champagne with oysters the day he keeled over in his office. Unlike Cassius and Brutus they didn't actually kill him with knives, but no one ever cared for Caesar, did they? He had too much power and it made him a tyrant, in the office and in the home. Let's hope Troy keeps a level head.'

'Troy is not like you!' Charmides snatched a chain of amber beads from her bed-table and began to worry them, clicking them through her fingers, her valuable rings sparkling and gleaming.

'Let's hope he isn't too much like Patir,' her son rejoined.

'I loved your father!' Charmides' voice, Wilda

noticed, had taken that rather off-key note of rising anger mixed with the self-pity of a lonely, spoiled woman who was the cause of most of her own misery. She could have travelled and enjoyed the world instead of choosing to laze about in a silk-hung bedroom, indulging her body with sweets and her mind with bitter memories. That some of them were bitter, Wilda had long since guessed. Charmides had enjoyed material luxury, but a real and passionate love had been withheld from her, and Wilda found herself looking at Damien and wondering just how much he was like his Greek father.

At the moment he was regarding his mother with a steely look in his eyes.

'I wonder what you mean by love?' he said to her. 'I suppose love can be as tormenting as it can be exhilarating—the trouble was, I missed seeing any of the tenderness which I imagine compensates for the torment.'

'Helios was not a man to show his feelings, except in private!' Charmides' fingers were grasping the beads as if she wanted to break the silver on which they were strung. Wilda wanted to ask Damien to leave the room, to leave the house and not come like this, churning everything up with his disturbing remarks and his knowledge of things that both she and his mother wished to remain buried in the past.

'Ah, his feelings.' Damien looked entirely sardonic, even as his gaze shifted to the worry beads that were clicking away nervously in his mother's fingers. 'We share those with the beasts and the birds, but surely love between a man and a woman should hold something more than the instinct for race survival?' His eyes slid in Wilda's direction ... like a silver blade

34

sliding across her creamy throat, and she shivered involuntarily.

'I once had an idea that they might—shades of Tristan and Isolde, eh? How youthful ideals get knocked about by disillusion!'

'You aren't a romantic,' his mother said scornfully. 'You take your pleasures as they come!'

'Denying me a few dreams, *manoula mou*?'

Charmides gave him an uncertain look, and the beads ceased their clicking. 'Is there a girl, Damien? Have you come home to tell me you have found her at last?'

He shrugged his shoulders. 'I did meet someone, but nothing is certain. I have to do battle with a matter of —prejudice.'

'Not her parents? They aren't prejudiced against you, are they?'

'No.' He said it briefly. 'But I don't wish to discuss the matter just yet. I have to think about my intentions —whether they are serious, you understand? Moonside seemed the logical place, where I wouldn't be distracted by business concerns.'

'But you must know if you want to marry the girl.' Charmides gave him a look of exasperation mingled with curiosity. 'What is she called and where does she come from?'

'I'm not going to tell you, dear Mother.' His smile was ironical. 'You might disapprove of my choice and upset the cherry cart. I won't have that until my mind is made up and then it won't matter a hoot in hell if you approve or not.'

'Is she pretty?' For an instant Charmides' gaze dwelt on the portrait of herself that hung on the bedroom wall, and a tiny gleam of complacency came into her eyes, as if she doubted that either of her sons would find a girl as beautiful as she had been in her heyday.

'Really quite lovely,' he drawled, following his mother's gaze to the portrait. 'It could be only a physical response that I feel—I have to find out.'

'She isn't a—worldly girl, one you've met at some international resort? You know the type, Damien! I want for you a girl of virtue, and I don't care if it is an old-fashioned word and a near impossibility in this day and age! Is she worthy to join this family?'

'Virtue?' he murmured, his eyes narrowing so that the grey irises were shadowed by his black lashes. 'I wonder, is it all right for a man to sow wild oats but all wrong for a woman? God, I'm cursed by the Greek instincts in my very bones. I want her responsive, but I want her good!'

'Don't you know if she's good and decent?' his mother demanded.

'This girl, *manoula mou*, is sweet hell on a pair of seductive legs. I feel I could entirely lose my head over her, but at the same time I could throttle her for upsetting all my notions of love. I'm no saint and have never pretended to be, but I never expected to react like a damned prig!'

He flung out his hands in a very Greek gesture. 'If there was one thing I never was, it was a prim moralist ever ready to condemn others for being only human. But suddenly I come across a girl and she has the eyes of an angel and the instincts of an alley cat——'

'What?' Charmides barely breathed the word. 'You dare to tell me you are thinking of marrying a—a *fille de joie*?'

'She isn't exactly one of those.' He gave a gravelly

36

laugh, but his eyes were not amused. 'This is my life, little mother, and I choose my own wife. If I do decide I want this girl, then she will be well taught that she never goes astray ever again.'

'Damien,' his mother spoke his name in a voice of doom, 'this girl is not a virgin?'

'No.' He spoke briefly. 'I have to come to terms with that fact, but you can dismiss it. And you can take that outraged Victorian look off your maternal face. It doesn't go with mascara, rouge and lilac hair.'

'How dare you!' Suddenly Charmides lost her temper entirely and flung her worry beads directly at his face. He reacted swiftly and with a lithe movement was at the door and opening it. 'I am going to have some breakfast. Why don't you get out of that bed and come for a spin in my new car? It has an Italian body and a Rolls-Royce soul. Superb!'

'Go to the devil where you belong and take that little harlot with you! If you dare marry her——'

'I shall marry whom I please,' he taunted. 'But who said I was going that far? I have to think about it. I may only want to take her'—he paused and laughed significantly, 'to dinner.'

He closed the bedroom door decisively behind him, leaving his mother in a seething rage. 'Devil—rake—hell-bound son of Satan!' she screamed after him, and snatching a hand-mirror from the bed-table she hurled it at the door, shatteringly. 'I was a decent girl—Helios was proud of me even if he didn't often show he—cared. Love? Is love supposed to be everything?'

'Madame,' Wilda leaned over Charmides and took hold of her hands that were plucking the pink sheets, trying to soothe them, and at the same time trying not to reveal the tumult of her own nerves. 'Your son is a grown man and he must go his own way. He isn't a little boy any more. He knows if he plays with fire he's likely to get burned.'

'What would you know?' Charmides flung in Wilda's face. 'You're a single young woman and you don't go out with men. You're probably frigid! I bore two sons, and that one—that one who has just gone laughing out of that door—he took hours to come into the world and he hurt me then, and he's gone on hurting me ever since. He had such charming ways, and then he and Helios started to fight, and it was hell, I tell you! Too much alike! That was the trouble, the cause of it all. Proud, hard, and Greek to their marrow. Thank God my other son was less demanding—less charismatic. I pity the girl, if he's set on her! But such a girl! Her body already used by someone else! How can he do this to me?'

'Love isn't a reasonable emotion, madame, and it sounded to me as if your son has some feeling for the girl. It's his life, as he pointed out.'

'A life he wouldn't have if I hadn't gone through the agony of giving him birth.'

Wilda could have pointed out that Charmides had beforehand gone through the pleasure of conceiving him, but she felt that too much had been said already and the flames of anger and resentment had to be banked down even if they went on smouldering.

'Shall I ring for your breakfast, madame? Some hot sweet coffee and something to eat will do wonders for your nerves—oh, I realise you're upset, and I do understand that even grown-up children can still cause heartache.' Wilda gave a slight smile. 'I'm not made of ice because I keep myself to myself.'

'What are you made of, I wonder?' Charmides stared

at her. 'You're too good-looking not to have a boy-friend. Has your heart been broken at some time?'

The question shook Wilda and perhaps at any other time she might have confided her secret trouble to Charmides, but right now was not the time to talk about Monte Carlo and a divorce based not on reality but on a cruel and cunning fiction.

'Yes,' Charmides sighed, 'I will have coffee and perhaps a couple of *croissants*, and eggs with a slice of smoked ham, and don't forget the toast. Tell Inez to bring up my tray, and you go and have your own breakfast—Wilda.' The plump, lilac-tipped hands clung to the slender ones with unpainted fingernails. 'What must you think of my son coming home like this, with such unhappy news for his poor mother—it's a wonder my poor heart can take it! Wanting a girl like that, who he brazenly admits is no better than a *coquette*. He's doing it on purpose, to get even with me for being on the side of his father over the matter of not doing his duty by going into the family business. It wouldn't have hurt him, to please Helios, but he's so self-willed and obstinate and once he's made his mind up about something there's just no shifting him— why, it would be like trying to snatch a meat bone from a tiger! He'll go ahead and marry that girl, I just feel it in my bones.'

As she said this Charmides groaned and gave a very good imitation of Saint Joan surrounded by the burning faggots. 'Ah, my poor aching back! Car rides, indeed! When you've eaten, Wilda, come and give my spine a massage with those slim cool hands of yours.'

'Yes, madame.' Wilda smiled, but found herself agreeing in her mind with Damien that a sunlit spin in a comfortable car, along the coastal road, would do

39

Charmides far more good than giving in to aches of the body and heart that weren't relieved by staying cooped up in her bedroom, no matter how beautifully appointed with its ceiling mouldings of peach and cream, and its furniture fit for a French palace. She would eat a large breakfast, have herself massaged, and then smoke her way through a pack of Chesterfields while reading magazine articles on beauty and fashion.

'I'll fetch your tray if you like,' Wilda offered.

'No, child, you go and have a break in the garden, and ignore that *nudnik* if you see him.'

'It is your son Troy who is the *macher*, eh?' Wilda's eyes were smiling as they met her employer's.

'So you know a little Yiddish, *hein*? From where?'

'My father worked among musicians, many of whom were deliciously funny men, and so kind-hearted.' Wilda suppressed a sign, remembering Kenny Devine who had liked her and advised her not to go and sing at the Hotel St Cyr. He had wanted to take care of her by marrying her after her father died, but she had been young and wildly romantic, and all she had felt for Kenny was the affection of a sister.

'There is more to you, my girl, than meets the eye.' Charmides stared with abrupt curiosity at her maid-companion. 'A man has hurt you, I think. Be well advised and don't let it happen again.'

'I don't intend to, madame.' Wilda was briefly tempted to confide in her employer and be free of that nagging suspicion that Damien Demonides meant to torment her subtly with his knowledge of what had supposedly happened at Monte Carlo, but the next instant Charmides had reached for her jewel-box and rather like a spoiled girl was consoling herself with her costly toys. 'Run along, Wilda. Have your breakfast in the garden among the innocent birds and bees, and forget the damage that love does to our foolish hearts. Remain wise, young one, and keep men out of your life.'

Wilda intended to remain wise ... a resolve that was cruelly shaken when she arrived at the table in the walled garden and found one of the cane chairs occupied by a male figure in a tan shirt and cream slacks, busily eating his way through a mixed grill of kidneys, bacon, mushrooms and eggs lightly fried on both sides.

He rose from his chair and waited until she had sat down, then he gave her a quizzical look and gestured at the silver domes over the food. 'Help yourself while everything is still hot. I gather you always eat breakfast under the hibiscus trees?'

'Yes,' she said, pouring a cup of coffee and feeling the nerves doing a step-dance around her midriff. She had stepped through the little iron gate into this secluded area she so liked before realising that Damien was here ... she would have retreated quickly had she seen him before he glanced round from the table. Then to retreat would have looked cowardly, and shown him that she was a little scared of him and the ruthlessness that was in the very lines of his body.

'It really is a splendid morning,' he said sociably. 'Florida at this time of the year can hardly be bettered —unless, of course, a hurricane should strike.'

'Are you expecting one, Mr Demonides?' she asked, in a cool voice, helping herself to sausages and eggs.

'I might ask the same question of you, Wilda Bird. Are you expecting the arrival of a destructive force from out of the blue?'

'I think it arrived last night,' she retorted, breaking a triangle of crisp toast and applying butter. 'You've

41

certainly stirred your mother up, haven't you? Was it your deliberate intention to do so?'

'Quite the *dame de compagnie*, aren't you? Is the concern for my mother really genuine?'

'It most certainly is.' Her eyes flashed. 'But I very much doubt if sympathy and tolerance are within the realms of your understanding.'

'It amazes me that they're part of your psyche,' he drawled. 'Do eat your eggs before they become congealed. I'm sure a vital young woman like yourself has a good appetite—what a pity I can't take you for a spin in my car. Do you think my mother would have a fit if I kidnapped you for a few hours?'

'Your mother would fire me, Mr Demonides, and that is what you'd like to happen.'

'Would I really?' His gaze drifted about the walled garden and rested on the arch of honeysuckle high as a man, with trumpet-shaped flowers climbing masses of green tendrils and oval leaves, the vivid scent attracting the honey bees. 'The castle flower,' his tone of voice had become half-honeyed and his gaze returned to Wilda and dwelt on her hair. 'How stunningly fair you are! Every inch the *anglika*, aren't you? So much the deceptive ice-flower.'

'You can keep your back-handed compliments to yourself,' Wilda said, icily. 'I don't fancy them with my breakfast, thank you.'

'How about supper?' he drawled.

'Not at any time of the day, so don't waste your breath on any more false flattery.' Wilda chewed sausage and glanced away from him, but was all the time aware of his eyes upon her profile. 'And do stop watching me eat—it isn't feeding time at the zoo!'

He gave a brief laugh and lifted the coffee pot. 'I

shall do with you what I damn well please,' he said, deliberately. 'More coffee?'

'You'll do what?' Her shocked eyes found his face.

'You heard me, Wilda Bird.'

'Really——!' She was lost for an adequate reply to his statement and wanted it to be a really cutting one when her breath and her wits were in full use again ... right now she felt as if she were gaping like a stranded fish ... it would be hopelessly Victorian to ask him how he dared to say such a thing. There was a wicked sensuousness in his eyes that warned her of his daring nature.

'Yes, really.' He refilled her cup and swirled cream into the aromatic coffee. 'Have you the muscle to stop me, or even the true inclination? You know as well as I that the marauding hornet is always attracted to the sweetest piece of fruit.'

'D—do you imagine I'm attracted to you?' she gasped.

'You're intrigued, *melle mou*, as you're bound to be when we share a secret that would shock my mother to her backbone. Does she ever leave that Queen Anne bed to come downstairs?'

'Not often——' Wilda had to hold her coffee cup with both hands, so jumpy were her nerves. Attracted to him? It was true he had a potent physical attractiveness; that he exuded *élan vital* from every pore of his supple brown body, but he was heartless, and she never wanted to fall into the hands of a cruel man ever again.

'Don't you attempt to persuade my mother to leave her room?' he demanded. 'What does she do all day, eat chocolates and paint her fingernails?'

'I'm only her maid, remember.' Wilda gave him a

43

resentful look. 'I can't give orders to someone who pays my wages.'

'She must be persuaded to leave that scented bed-room—I had no idea she had developed into a semi-invalid until Troy wrote to tell me she had a semi-nurse living in at Moonside—a young woman by the name of Wilda. When did you ever do nursing?'

'I worked as a nurse-aide before coming to Moonside to work.'

'How noble of you, Wilda.'

'Don't sneer, *kyrie*, it doesn't go with your nose, which is rather more noble than you are!'

'There,' he casually lit a Cuban cheroot and puffed the agreeable smoke into the air. 'I said you were at-tracted to me.'

'I once admired a panther at the zoo, but I felt no inclination to put my arms around him.'

'Do you feel an urge to put them around me?'

'I'd be in equal danger of being mauled.'

'Some *filles de joie* keep a razor in their garter-belt, but you keep yours in your tongue, don't you, honey?'

'I've learned that it pays.' Wilda felt she hated him for what he had called her, but as he lounged there in the cane chair, lazily enjoying his cheroot, she felt her eyes sliding across the taut power of his shoulders in the tan shirt. Yes, she told herself, he was like a panther, unpredictable, and at times savagely hurtful. Her gaze fell away from him and she prodded a mushroom she no longer felt like eating.

'Women are a little like mushrooms,' he remarked. 'Some have virtue, while others are quite virulent. Some give satisfaction, while others destroy.'

'Virtue seems to buzz in your bonnet like a persistent hornet,' she rejoined. 'Is it because you have so little of that commodity yourself?'

'I might be quite nice, a few skins deep.'

'You aren't very nice to your mother, Mr Demonides. You were teasing her unmercifully over that girl, but I don't believe you'd ever marry a woman who had been possessed by some other man. Your pride wouldn't be able to take it—you'd make her life a torment.'

'What makes you so sure about me and my pride?'

'It's Greek pride, inherited from your father. I think you're a second edition of Helios Demonides.'

'My father wouldn't have sat here and allowed a chit of an English girl speak to him as you are speaking to me. He'd have dressed you down.'

'In that respect you probably differ—your eyes, Mr Demonides, undress a woman!'

'How naughty of them.'

'I—I don't like it!'

'Come, *melle mou*, you love to have your long creamy legs on display in nothing but a man's sleeping jacket. Nothing was ever invented that suited so well a shapely young creature, dragged from a cosy bed with her lovely hair all tousled and her eyes still love-dazed——'

'Stop it!' Unable to take any more from him, Wilda leapt to her feet and in doing so jarred the cane table, spilling coffee on to Damien's impeccable slacks. 'Oh, God—I've got to get away—from you!' She turned and began to run, but her legs were shaking and she was cruelly outpaced by him. He clamped a restraining hand upon her, holding her, his lips twisted into a savage smile.

'Let me go!' She said it through her teeth. 'I won't let you treat me like this—like some awful vamp!'

'You didn't expect me to treat you like a virgin, did you?'

'Damn your eyes!'

'The same goes for yours, little one. Blue as stained-glass windows, as the iris flower, and the cloak of the Madonna, and all the time—*I was there, honey.* I saw you with that greasy pig of a producer, the sweat still gleaming on his satisfied face! How could you let his sort lay even a little finger upon you?'

'He didn't—ever! It was all a ghastly plot and a nightmare—don't you understand? He drugged me! He put something in my tomato juice and I passed out!'

Damien gazed down at her, his face like an iron mask. 'Is that the truth, as God is your witness?'

'I hope to drop dead if it's a lie!'

'So you weren't willing—you didn't co-operate? He took you while you lay unconscious?'

'*No!*'

'Then what are you saying?'

'He didn't touch me—ever!'

Damien stared down at her tormented face, and then his lips twisted and he flung her away from him so her shoulder and arm struck the scaly trunk of a palm tree, causing her to gasp with pain. 'What your sort won't say when driven to it! He touched you all right—it was apparent to anyone who saw his wife drag you away from him, your hair all wanton and that damned purple jacket showing your legs to your thighs! There were bruises on you—I saw them with my own eyes!'

'Yes, I know.' Wilda stood there massaging the arm and shoulder he had just bruised. 'When I came to my senses his wife was beating at me with her handbag and it had bone handles. I—I happen to bruise very easily.'

'Sure, baby, I bet you do.' Damien swept his eyes up and down her figure, and it was all too apparent that he didn't believe a word of her story—just as no one else would have believed it. That was why she hadn't protested or argued, for the awful truth was that the newspaper reporters would have found the details of the true story even more toothsome for their readers— the headlines would have been graphic and shocking— girl singer raped while unconscious. It had seemed like the lesser of two evils to let everyone believe she had been having an affair with Myles Sadlier. Sexual affairs were two a penny, but who would have believed that a man like Sadlier had been alone with her, drugged and unprotesting, and denied himself the pleasure of making love to her? Only she had known that he had obeyed some unexpected scruple and after putting her into his pyjama jacket and his bed, had waited until his wife came to the suite and discovered them together. If her hair had been in disarray it was because Laura Sadlier had gripped it in her fist as she hauled Wilda, dazed and reeling, off the bed which Myles had deliberately rumpled.

Wilda shuddered at the memory and wanted to run away and hide from what was going through Damien's mind as he stood regarding his half-smoked cheroot with brooding eyes. It had all come rushing back, the shame and mortification of that night, and suddenly she felt like giving way to tears, hard racking ones that would bring some relief and yet destroy remnants of pride this man had left her.

She fought back the tears and at last was able to say: 'I'll leave your mother's house. I can't stay at Moonside with this cloud hanging over me.'

She was turning away when his voice arrested her. 'No,' he said, and when she turned to look at him his jaw was still a thing of iron, but the angry contempt had gone out of his eyes as if something forlorn in her attitude had touched him just a little. 'I can't let you walk out on my mother. She's a lonely woman and she has become accustomed to having your company. I think it better if you stay.'

Wilda shook her head. 'I think it better if I go, Mr Demonides.'

'Why, because of me?' He drew on his cheroot and then stubbed it out against the trunk of the palm tree, grinding it into the greeny-gold scales. 'I shall be gone in a while, and no doubt being found out the way you were has proved a traumatic lesson for you. If I allow you to leave Moonside I might be sending you back to—damnation.'

Wilda shivered ... it couldn't be denied that she didn't truly wish to leave this place which had become such a haven for her, and it was also true that Damien Demonides would soon grow restless for pastures new and he would pack his bags, kiss his mother goodbye, and drive off into the sunset.

Why should she let him drive her away?

'You'd better go to Charmides,' he said. 'She probably wants you for something—it's all right, I shan't let any bushy-tailed cats out of the bag. I can see how much you regret ever getting mixed up with a guy like Sadlier.'

His eyes dwelt on her face, which for all its soft suntan was waxen pale right now, her eyes densely blue and unhappy. 'And stop looking like a wet Monday or my mother might want to know what's wrong. She might assume that I've been tormenting you.'

'Such a thing never entered your mind, did it, Mr Demonides?' Wilda walked away from him, and never had her heart felt so heavy.

# CHAPTER THREE

In that Florida garden sloping to the sea there were many tropical trees including the *cherimoya*, which bore a delicious apple-like fruit. The most impressive was the royal palm, so tall and well-balanced on its silver-grey trunk, that towered over the other trees in a dominant way.

Wilda walked through the garden to where a small jetty was suspended above the fascinating. timeless beat of the ocean as it rolled in over the sands. Charmides no longer kept a boat, not since her sons had left home and there was no one any more who cared to go sailing on the waters around the Keys.

A tangy breeze blew towards Wilda and tossed her hair from side to side, and she gazed as if tranced at the sea pounding in over the rocks and gradually wearing them to grains of sand. Like the forces of life, like the beating of a great heart, driven to seek its purpose against all odds and to have its way with the rocks and the soft sand beyond them.

Her feet were bare and white against the bare rock splashed by the spume, for she had not long emerged from her swim and her hair was still damp around her neck and she wore only a short towelling jacket that came to the tops of her thighs. She felt fairly safe and secure right now, for Charmides had said that Damien was going out to dine, and by the time she returned to the house he would have left, speeding away in his black car that was somehow like a condor when it took off, and made no sound because a beautiful Rolls-Royce engine lay inside the sleek chassis.

She took deep breaths of the pure air and tilting back her head half-closed her eyes in order to savour her sense of freedom that at this moment was so atuned to the untamed freedom of the ocean ... her arms moved open as if to collect it to her heart ... she yearned for something which had no name because she didn't dare to give it one.

All around her the late afternoon was sheened with a raw gold haze, lovely and melancholy, with a hint of flame creeping into the sky. Soon the flame would sweep over the gold, burning it out of the sky until all that was left was darkness and gradually the gleaming stars.

'So must Daphne have looked when the sun-god came upon her.'

The voice came suddenly ... a deep and seducing quality to its tones so that Wilda could be fooled into thinking how attractive a male voice could sound ... until she opened her eyes and saw 'the demon', as she thought of him.

He wore a dinner-jacket lined with wine-coloured silk, open against a white ruffled shirt and wine tie. Wilda's was the instinctive stillness of the hunted creature as her eyes met Damien's, and then his gaze flicked her figure, half revealed in the terrycloth jacket, which she quickly drew around her, feeling as if the embarrassed heat of her body would come right through the material. His gaze fell to her legs and with all her nerves she knew what was going through his mind ... what scene was being acted out again in his memory.

As if to echo Wilda's torment the waves struck upwards and broke weeping on the rocks, and as the sunset flared its pagan fire was captured in Damien's eyes, and Wilda felt the burning flush that swept over her body, making her shudder and clench her fingers in the cloth of her jacket.

'Are you really content to remain here as the companion of a rather spoiled and self-absorbed woman of my mother's age?' he asked. 'Don't you long to have the freedom that you see out there, where the sun is falling out of sight?'

'Your mother pays me a good salary——' And then the hurt resentment wouldn't be contained in her prosaic reply. 'What you're really saying is that it seems out of character for someone like me to want this kind of life after the tinsel glitter of the casinos and the jet set. Hasn't it occurred to you, *kyrie*, that this might be my real setting?'

As he remained silent a catamaran sailed by, graceful against the red horizon, its single sail soon lost in the deepening shadows. In the trees the cicadas were chirring and seabirds were flying in over the gilded scrolls of ocean. Nothing was still except Damien's face, which might have been carved from teak.

'Join me for dinner,' he said unexpectedly. 'I assume this is your evening off, as you aren't in uniform, and Charmides, when I looked in on her, was up to her fingertips in luscious chocolates and an enduring movie of Ronald Colman's.'

'But—I assumed you had a date already.' Wilda's heart had quickened in the most alarming way ... the last thing she had expected from him was an invitation to go out with him.

'I assure you I have no date.' He shot back his cuff, in which ebony studs gleamed darkly against the starched whiteness of his dinner shirt. 'But I do have a table booked at the Club Dinarzade for eight o'clock. We could just make it, if you aren't one of those women who takes an hour to fix her hair and her face.'

Wilda stood silent, unwilling to commit herself to either an acceptance of his invitation or a refusal. She was deeply resentful of the opinion he had of her, but she was also aware that they shared a mutual feeling of intrigue.

'No answer is almost a promise,' he murmured. 'Are you afraid to trust yourself in my company?'

'I'm not sure——'

'Oh, come, you don't need to search your soul before you agree to share dinner with a lonely man.'

'Lonely—you?'

'Yes, at this precise moment. Don't we all have our lonely times?'

'Being alone and bereft of feminine company isn't loneliness, *kyrie*.'

'Possibly true, then let's say I wish to share dinner with a lonely young woman.'

'Lonely—me?' She was mocking him for once. 'Whoever heard of a vamp being lonely?'

He quirked a black eyebrow and his hands dug into the pockets of his jacket. 'Let's call a *treva*?' he said. 'We live in the same house for the time being and we can't always be at each other's throats.'

'A truce?' she echoed.

'Yes, why not?'

'How long would it last? Until you felt like twisting everything I say to suit whatever you want to believe of me? A *treva* sounds nice, but you're as unpredictable as that panther I once saw behind bars, with his eyes glowing and his pelt rippling ... he looked as if he'd be marvellous to stroke, except that a notice warned people he was dangerous.'

'I'm a man, Wilda. I don't bite the hand that strokes me.'

'I—I don't think it would work, going out with you.' Wilda went to turn away, but he seized her by the wrist and spun her to face him.

'Did you ever play the tables at Monte Carlo?' he asked.

'Yes, once or twice.' She gazed up at him and nerves fluttered in the depth of her stomach. 'I lost both times, so I can't be called a fortunate gambler.'

'Take one more gamble—it could be third time lucky.'

'No—your mother might need me!'

'Doesn't it mean a thing, *melle mou*, that I might need you?'

She actually cringed away from him when he said that ... or did she cringe away from herself? 'Y-you need me as a naughty boy needs a net when he sees a butterfly—leave my wings alone, *kyrie*, they've been singed enough and I—I couldn't take any more!'

He stared down into her eyes, a deep aching blue with a deep wave of breeze-blown hair falling into them. 'The devil of it is, Wilda, that I can't promise to be a good boy. It's been too long since I tried—but are you so spiritless now that you won't take a chance on me? What can I do to you in a crowded restaurant, with waiters buzzing around and people dancing to today's unromantic music?'

'I—I haven't been to a restaurant in a long time——' Wilda could feel herself weakening, and she could also feel his fingers pressing against the pulse in her wrist, checking for himself his effect on her emotions. She was young and very much a female, and the protective width of a man's shoulders could lessen her grip on self-reliance and her resolve never to trust another man as long as she lived. She wanted to pull away from him and dash back through the garden to the safety of Moonside, but his fingers tightened as if he sensed her impulse, and he was many times stronger ... a whole lot more ruthless than she.

'Dress up for once and forget that drab uniform that Charmides insists on making you wear.' His voice was low, gravelly, coming from deep in his brown throat. 'Surely you have an evening dress?'

'Yes——'

'Then come along and get dressed up to kill. It will do you good to get away from Moonside for a few hours.' Gripping her by the hand he made her walk with him along the garden path, where the flowers and foliage gave off a heady scent now the heat of the day was over. The cicadas, no longer sun-stunned, were filling the night with their chirring, and Wilda felt the coolness against her bare legs as she stretched them in order to keep up with Damien's impetuous stride. Her body wanted to be with him in that restaurant, but her mind reacted against the urge. It was the panther again, moving close to the bars and inviting a reckless hand to fondle him ... then snap would go the animal white teeth and scaring pain would follow the pleasure.

Yet Wilda walked with him along the *chemin de ronde* into the house by a side door ... the wall walk had been shadowy, but here in the hall the lights were on and Wilda didn't want to look into Damien's eyes in case they glowed with expectancy like the panther's.

Yes, she wanted to dine and dance, to be uncaring and unquestioning, and still without looking at him, she said breathlessly, 'I—I'll go and get ready. I'm not one of those who takes an hour.'

'I didn't think so,' he murmured. 'You don't need an hour.'

She sped away from him the moment he released her hand, and once inside her room she had to rest for a few moments against the closed door. It was crazy, what she was doing ... but somehow it was inevitable.

Having been in the sea she didn't need to shower, except to wash the sand grains from her feet. Her taut young figure needed only a very brief and lacy bra and as she clipped it on, her cheeks grew warm because she had felt ... actually felt the touch of Damien's eyes when her beach jacket had fallen open. Was that why he had asked her to go out with him, because he had discovered that now and again she swam in the nude? In lace-trimmed panties and slip she went to the mirror and combed her hair, shining it with a strip of silk and fastening into the smooth side of it a sparkling clip. She zipped herself into a silk-jersey dress in a smoky-blue, finely pleated from the hips downward. Across her throat she fastened a strand of pure gold, the last present she had ever received from her father, bought in Paris when she was eighteen, when she had just begun to suspect that he hadn't much longer to live.

Wilda ran her fingertips along the golden necklace and a sigh caught her by the throat. He was the only man who had ever cared about her as a person ... other men only noticed that she had pale hair with a soft thickness to it, and a slim, gracefully curved body.

The chinoiserie mirror gave back this pleasing reflection to her, and there was something in her eyes that made them incandescent ... eyes that wanted to be happy ... eyes that also wanted to cry.

Round her shoulders she draped a chenille scarf, a poor substitute for a stylish evening cape, but when she had decided to work in the States, and especially here at Key Laguda, she had sold a lot of her nice things, having made up her mind to live the kind of life that would not include parties.

She checked her little silver bag to make sure she had a handkerchief, a comb and her powder-case, not forgetting a little wad of dollars just in case she needed to come home in a cab!

When she looked in on her employer the tension relaxed from her lips and she found herself smiling. Charmides lay at ease on her pink lounger with her eyes fixed upon the screen of the white-cased television. 'Such a charming movie,' she said, without shifting her gaze one fraction of an inch in Wilda's direction. 'What a handsome man that Britisher was—you come of a good-looking race of people, child. Good breeding shows itself in the bones and the eyes—mmm, just listen to that beautiful speaking voice! He loves the girl, you see, but he doesn't realise she's his wife because his memory has got all mixed up in the great war and in a streetcar accident. So very sad! I've been having a lovely weep—they don't make movies like this one any more!'

Wilda's smile deepened and she watched a moment while Charmides dreamily tipped ash from a small cigar into the box of Swiss chocolates, then she quietly withdrew and was relieved that her employer hadn't noticed that she was wearing a long dress and T-strapped silver shoes.

Charmides would enjoy the film to the full, eat her supper of chicken sandwiches, and then drift off to sleep. Only when in pain did she require a sleeping pill, but strangely enough she had not complained of backache for the past ten days ... Wilda wondered if it had something to do with Damien being here at Moonside. He kept his mother's mind on other things ... and still he teased her about this marriage to a girl whom Charmides refused to consider suitable for even her reprobate son, as she called him.

Only last night Wilda had heard her say to Damien that Helios would turn over in his grave if a son of his went to the altar with a girl who was nothing more or less than 'soiled goods'. 'Helios always had first choice,' Charmides had said cuttingly. 'From an air-flight ticket down to a watermelon! Have you gone out of your mind, Damien? When did you ever marry a girl you can have for nothing? You haven't given her a baby, have you? That would be the final indignity!'

Damien had laughed in that way of his, never out loud, but deep inside him where it had a lot more meaning.

When Wilda arrived at the foot of the stairs he was there waiting for her and over his arm he carried something that glimmered softly against the dark barathea of his dinner-jacket. With his free hand he reached out and removed the chenille scarf from Wilda's shoulders. 'I want you to wear this,' he said. 'I somehow had an idea that you hadn't come to Moonside kitted out for evenings on the town—turn around just a little so I can help you on with it.'

It was a long cloak of dove-grey velvet to which clung a faint and expensive scent. A cowl was attached, trimmed with soft grey fur. He stroked the fur as he settled the cloak around Wilda's figure. 'My mother has clothes all over the house—rich women are terrific hoarders—and I found this in one of her wardrobes.

From the style she probably wore it during the early years of her marriage, but it's still almighty glamorous, eh?'

It was beautiful and incredibly supple to the fingers, and Wilda couldn't control a tremor deep inside her when Damien framed her face and hair in the fur-trimmed cowl. He gazed down into her eyes, holding the fur around her face.

'It has to be admitted ... to look at you're the loveliest creature I ever took anywhere. You have a rare essence, Wilda Bird. A magic even my cynical nature isn't proof against. Some women have beautiful faces but bad posture; others have perfect figures but sulky features. The devil stirred into you all the correct ingredients and you emerged a lovely glowing thing ... your parents must have adored you and kept you on a close rein, so that when it was released—how long has your father been dead?'

'Nearly four years——' Wilda found herself unbearably close to Damien, lost in the mesmerism of his grey eyes, pulsating right through the velvet of the dove-grey cloak.

'Then at Monte Carlo—?' His raised eyebrow asked the remainder of his question.

'Please—let it rest!' Her eyes pleaded for his mercy, her lips half-parted, and his eyes narrowed to smoky slits as he gazed at her mouth.

'Your mother, where is she?' Not much mercy was in Damien's nature and the look on his face was inexorable.

'In Provence with her second husband.'

'So to all intents and purposes you're alone in the world?'

'You could say that,' she sighed.

'Wilda Bird, set free and at the mercy of the hawks—I've been a damnable brute to you, haven't I?'

'Yes.'

'God, but you're lovely!' His eyes were so sensuous that it was for Wilda like being touched, except that he didn't remove his hands from the fur-trimmed cowl.

'You shouldn't say such things, Mr Demonides.' There was that other girl he had to marry, and Wilda couldn't speak of her—the words just wouldn't come.

'And why not?' he drawled. 'Doesn't every woman like to be told of her desirability?'

'It isn't right when the man——' Wilda bit her lip. 'Didn't you tell your mother you were thinking of getting married? Didn't you imply that there was s-some reason for it being imperative?'

'Ah yes, so I did. Thank you for reminding me, but it goes to show that I may not be a marrying man.'

'I shouldn't think the sacrament of marriage has much meaning for you, *kyrie*.' She hesitated. 'In the loving sense, that is.'

'All in all to one another, one woman and one man, in joy and tribulation, eh?'

'You'd feel exactly like the panther, prowling back and forth in your cage and ready to bite through the bars with your strong teeth.'

'Yes.' He gave a brief laugh. 'I daresay you're right, but I think I may have to marry the girl despite everything and bring down on my head more tribulation than real joy—unhallowed joy, with no doubts and no regrets.'

At these words Wilda felt a stab deep down in the vitals of her body—a shock, electric and painful. Then what his mother had surmised was correct ... Damien had got the girl into trouble, and being more Greek than anything else he was going to put the matter right, and as the son of a Greek he would probably regard marriage as entirely binding and not to be got free from, as Myles Sadlier had got his release from a wife he had grown tired of.

Damien would marry if he had to, but Wilda doubted if he'd be a good husband if he didn't love his wife with an absorbing passion ... to him, as she had said, the sacrament would be but a means to an end.

Wilda thought fleetingly of Charmides ... she would never forgive Damien when she found out the truth, for she had not moved with the times and her moral attitudes were rooted in the days of her own girlhood, when it was permitted to tease a man but never to surrender her body until the priest let him in through the bedroom door.

'Why are you looking shocked, Wilda?' The words came soft and gravelly against her cheekbone.

'Should you be taking me out to dine?' Wilda drew carefully away from him. 'Let's call it off——'

'Be damned to that! Quite frankly, *melle mou*, I can't see what's so wrong in giving my mother's companion a meal at a smart restaurant. You've earned a break, haven't you?'

'I—I just don't want any more—trouble.'

'By trouble I take it you mean scandal? I'm not yet a married man!'

'But you're going to be, aren't you?' she demanded.

'Yes, I do believe I'm caught, and must accept my medicine. It could be rather sweet, if I don't choke over the sediment at the bottom of the cup. That's the pity of it.'

'Judge not, that ye be not judged,' she murmured.

'In other words, Wilda, my house is made of glass, eh?'

'I shouldn't aim any more stones, *kyrie*.'

'Then I shall aim a kiss instead.' He lowered his head and before Wilda could move he had laid his lips against her mouth ... lips that were warm, boldly defined, with a tang of the best tobacco on his breath. But more than that was the electrifying tingle they sent through Wilda to her very bones; a warning—if one was needed—that in a closer embrace she would experience the kind of feelings she had heard about but not yet felt for herself.

She jerked away from Damien and there was a look in her eyes that begged him not to treat her as he believed Myles Sadlier had treated her.

'You're right,' he drawled. 'We shall be late and lose our table at the Dinarzade.'

Under the folds of the cloak his hand found her elbow, and realising it would be useless to protest, Wilda went with him to his sleek black car, its interior upholstered in beige glove-leather, with cognac carpet underfoot.

So self-assured, this man Damien Demonides. So successful in his chosen career. So aware of women and their needs, and yet he had got himself trapped by precisely the type of girl he believed Wilda to be. The irony of it made a painful smile come and go about Wilda's mouth, moving the lips on which lingered the touch of Damien's, the hint of fire and the taste of his tobacco.

She slid into a seat that was entirely comfortable, and when Damien entered the car and closed the door, she felt not only the physical touch of him, but a mixture of apprehension and excitement, as if he had given her a strong wine to drink.

He glanced at her, his grey eyes smoking through his black lashes, and his look was directed at her lips as if he were still feeling them, soft and red and afraid to respond.

'What you must have been like at nineteen,' he murmured. 'The fates didn't arrange our meeting too well, did they?'

He started the car and they slid noiselessly down the palm-lined drive of Moonside, turning on to the highway that led into the main part of Key Laguda, the villa being several miles on the outskirts.

No, Wilda thought bleakly. At nineteen she had been very much alone, with no unearned scandal attached to her name. She would have been nervous of what Damien aroused in her, but he would not have been contemptuous of her, and he might even have been tender towards her vulnerability. Now it had all come too late! He couldn't wipe from his memory that scene at the St Cyr. And she must not forget that somewhere he had a girl who needed him to marry her. Bitter, stinging reminders for both of them, even as they sat within inches of each other in the intimacy of his car, driving smoothly along a highway above the seashore, with the moon curving like a silver blade in the velvety sky.

Wilda stole a look at Damien's profile and found it firm and distant and faintly shadowed by the thrusting cheekbone. His thoughts seemed concentrated upon his driving and she could study him without him being aware ... and for the first time she admitted fully to herself that she found his strong dark looks dangerously attractive. She knew with every cell in her body that once burned by his Greek fire she would never come alive to any other man.

She cuddled down into the folds of the velvet cloak, as if seeking a hiding place from her thoughts, but like persistent hornets they wouldn't leave her alone and they went on buzzing about in her head. To love Damien would be unbearably exciting, but at the same time it would lead nowhere and leave her in another traumatic state of mind ... and body. Already she felt herself infatuated ... this inner tumult of her senses could only mean that she was poised on the edge of falling into his powerful arms, and it mustn't happen!

'You have gone very quiet.' He gave her a brief but intent look. 'You have nestled down into all that velvet and fur like a squirrel in its drey and I can see only your huge eyes and the tip of your nose. Of what are you thinking?'

'That I was right about you, *kyrie*. Like the panther you are unpredictable—you make me dislike you, and then you turn on your charm and here I am in your car when I should be at the villa, on hand in case your mother needs me for anything.'

'Inez is there and she's a capable person, besides which you shouldn't have to be on duty on your free evening. All work and no play——' There he broke off and his eyebrows slid together in a black line. 'Why is it that you induce in me certain feelings of protectiveness? It makes no sense! I look at you in that cloak and you seem all sweet innocence, as if you knew nothing at all of the passions of men. Balzac was so right when he stated that "a woman's virtue is man's greatest invention". If I didn't invent some virtue for you, and the way you go about the villa so cool and untouchable in

63

your uniform, I might break your neck for making me—want you.'

Wilda gasped, half-closed her eyes and felt a roaring in her brain and ears—the mental pain was acute, but at the same time the physical delight was overwhelming. Damien had said it with words, and with his eyes—he wanted her!

These disturbing emotions in her body were shared by him, and because he was a man he was having to apply intense pressure in order to keep control of those feelings. It gave her a sudden sense of power that was strangely pleasing—she could hurt him if she wished, as he was capable of hurting her. She could throw in his teeth that he was really little better than Myles Sadlier—that like other men he was at the mercy of his male desires despite the fact that he was promised to someone else.

They rounded a sweep of the highway and Wilda felt the turning of her heart . . . if the desire had been all on her side it would somehow have been pathetic, but Damien wanted her and she felt alive as never before. She also felt the intensification of danger, for he wasn't a man who was accustomed to putting a brake on his inclinations.

'What we want,' she said coolly, 'and what we get are two different things. I'm your mother's maid-companion and I like my job too much to have a flaming affair with you, Mr Demonides, to be left when you depart the villa like the remains of one of your half-smoked Havanas. I've learned my lesson the hard way, and I don't intend to fall a second time into the clutches of a—cruel man.'

She had said it deliberately, choosing the word with care, and knew it wasn't entirely unjust. Any woman he thought of as special would suffer the emotional torments of the damned if she didn't live up to his expectations; it was stamped into his demanding face. He admired her looks and desired her body ... but afterwards he'd break her heart and walk away from her because of what had happened at Monte Carlo. It was something he would never forget or forgive ... this man whose blood and bones were pure Greek.

'Yes, it's quite an impasse,' he drawled. 'I would like to stop this car right now, take you down to some dark cove on the beach and make passionate love to you. It wouldn't be rape, my dear. I'm a little too wise not to know that I disturb you as much as you disturb me.'

'It would be ridiculous if you weren't aware of your masculine appeal, *kyrie*. I'm quite sure there have been women all over the globe who have let you prove your *zoikos*.'

'You have also proved your appeal to men, haven't you, *melle mou*?' He spoke with sudden harshness. 'What is one more man to you?'

'What indeed?' she said, in a voice tense with concealed agony. 'Some *treva*, this! I said it would never work for us to call a truce.'

'God, you're right! We're like a pair of snarling jungle cats.' He gave a brief, unamused laugh. 'We're two people who could find heaven together and yet we give each other hell. We're one aching component torn in two—it's like Greek tragedy! I yearn for you, but the pride in me makes me snarl and rip you with unforgivable words. Passion and pride hold us together even as they tear us apart!'

'Take me home, Damien.'

'No, we are at the Dinarzade and I want my dinner.' He swung the car into the parking area of the smart-looking restaurant, which towered above the harbour of Key Laguda, spangled with the lights of its scenic elevator that moved up and down the side of the white walls like a glowing glass cage.

'I vow to be good for the rest of the evening ... that's all I can promise.' The last few words were almost groaned, and Damien sat a moment in tense silence, clenching the leathered wheel in front of him, his profile rigid in the dashboard glow. 'None of us ask to be the way we are—we all have to fight, work and love in our own peculiar way. It's a law of nature that we have to satisfy what is deeply instinctive in us—let's leave it at that.'

They left the car and the chirring of cicadas seemed loud in the night as they walked to the elevator, and through the fronds of palm trees slid the silvery scythe of the moon, cutting the darkness. The glass cage settled as they arrived at its doors and when they slid open Wilda stepped inside before Damien could touch her. The cage glided upwards and she could see all over the harbour with its vari-coloured lights on the yachts that were moored there, and beyond lay the silky sea, reflecting those lights so that they quivered.

'Beautiful sight, isn't it?' Damien murmured, but his eyes were upon her, and she drew the velvet cloak against her, a gesture he couldn't mistake for it was entirely instinctive ... that of a woman who knows she is with a man who could conquer her.

'Wonderful,' she replied, gazing out of the glass walls and feeling an alarming sensation of being suspended among the stars as the cage drew nearer to the rooftop restaurant where they were obviously going to dine. Wilda had never been to the Club Dinarzade before, and now she realised that it was probably the swankiest restaurant on this part of the coast and she had a sudden suspicion that Damien had not booked a table here with the intention of dining alone.

She gave him a wondering look through her lowered lashes ... had he planned all along to bring her with him? Had he been so sure that she would agree to come?

The elevator settled and when they stepped out into the lighted foyer attached to the dining-room an attendant came at once to take her cloak, while a waiter appeared to lead them to their table.

## CHAPTER FOUR

THEIR table was beside a window and secluded by a lovely Persian screen, and Wilda felt a fluttering in her stomach for people were turning to look at Damien and herself as if they made a striking couple, he so tall, dark and assured, she so fair in contrast to him, reaching only to his shoulder in her silver kid shoes and smoke-blue dress.

When the waiter drew out her chair she was glad to sit down, for her legs felt oddly shaky. It had been a long time since she dined out with a man, and only Damien had ever touched so deep a chord of response within her, making her feel excited and yet at the same time very unsure. Her father had been adoring and protective, very careful to keep her from contact with anyone he distrusted. Kenny Devine had been rather shy of her, as if almost afraid to touch her.

She didn't make Damien feel shy, for that was a state

67

of mind and body he had never experienced in his life. She watched him discuss the wine list with their waiter, for they had both agreed to have lobster *flambé* to start with, the shellfish along this coast being always fresh caught and delicious. Having ordered their white wine he sat back in his chair and regarded Wilda with a slight smile that didn't remove the intentness from his grey eyes.

'I am going to repeat myself,' he murmured. 'You have breathtaking skin and hair tones, do you realise that? You also have a lovely shape, and I am being envied by nearly every male in this room, and those I exclude are with their boy-friends.'

'Your compliments are always double-edged.' She couldn't control a breathless laugh, even as she glanced around and wondered how he could tell the deviates from the real men; not all men were as obviously dominant as himself. 'Only prosperous people dine here, don't they? It's very ritzy.'

'Don't worry.' He quirked an eyebrow. 'No one would take you for a mother's help. I like your taste in dresses and I do believe this is the first time I've seen you out of uniform—no, I must correct myself!' His eyes glinted and Wilda knew instantly that he was recalling the way she had looked in her terrycloth beach jacket.

'Being utterly male,' he said, 'I can't imagine being enamoured of another body like my own. I prefer the silky skin, the warmth and wonder of a woman's body. Is it possible, *pedhaki mou*, that you are blushing?'

She was too confused to answer him and glanced away, fixing her eyes on the Persian screen that glowed with colour and imagery. In Greek he had called her his little one ... but she wasn't his and didn't intend to let him overwhelm her with his dark, seducing charm that would turn to cold indifference after he had thrust his way inside her defences.

'What a gorgeous screen,' she remarked. 'How those figures seem to glow with a life of their own.'

'It probably came from a *seraglio*, perhaps from the divan room of the pasha.' There was a taunting note in Damien's voice, as if he knew very well that he could take possession of her any time he chose, with all the ease with which he might light up a Cuban cheroot and smoke it to the stub, tossing carelessly aside what was left . . . or grinding it beneath his heel.

Wilda gave a little shudder that was all the more painful because it tremored inside her. To be possessed by Damien would be an overpowering experience, and though physically she might clamour for it, she shrank mentally from the aftermath . . . the prospect of abandonment after he had obeyed his conquering impulse, striding away from her, impelled towards someone to whom he owed a debt of honour.

She was glad when the waiter came to the table with their lobster, beautifully seasoned and set afire with rum. King of the sea lobster, the waiter informed them.

'Crack the legs for madame,' Damien requested. Their wine arrived, and he nodded that it be poured without the pretentious ritual of tasting it first; he knew in advance that it came from a first-class cellar and there probably wasn't a pretentious bone in his strong body. Wilda had to like that about him, that he was utterly honest with her, with everyone, never concealing his intentions behind a façade of false empathy —as Myles Sadlier had done.

He made no pretence of loving her . . . he wanted to enjoy her, just as he did the delicious lobster meat dug from the cracked bones with a little silver prong; just as he savoured the pale sparkling wine. '*Kali oreki*,' he raised his wine glass to her. 'Admit now that you are glad you came with me to the Dinarzade.'

'You intended that I should come, didn't you?' She felt in her fingers the silky smoothness of her wine glass, and saw beyond the windows of the club the panorama of Key Laguda, a chain of coloured lights that followed the undulations of the coastline, gradually falling away into the silky depths of the sea.

'Yes,' Damien admitted. 'I wanted you to myself, looking as lovely as I knew you could look out of that puritanical uniform. After we have eaten our food and finished that bottle of wine, we are going to dance together on the terrace, in the old-fashioned way. This is also a gaming club, if you haven't already guessed, and I am going to prove to you that you can win if you set your mind to it.'

'All planned, Damien, down to the last detail?'

'Yes, as a matter of fact.' He broke dark crusty bread and looked so eminently sure of himself that Wilda felt the excited apprehension mount inside her.

'That was Napoleon's downfall,' she said tensely. 'He planned every battle in advance but didn't take into account the unexpected.'

'Meaning?' Damien held the lobster prong, speared through a piece of white meat, halfway to his lips.

'The lobster's lovely, Damien, and I like the wine and the drifting music from the dance terrace. I'll gamble with you, if you want that—but unexpectedly I won't let you stop your car on the way home so that you can prove to yourself that I'm everything you have called me. The Russian snows were Napoleon's stumbling block ... they froze his soldiers and he had to retreat. You're an impressive man, Damien, and I'm sure you can be very ruthless in the pursuit of what you want, but I don't think you'd enjoy the empty victory of doing to me what you believe another man did.'

'Seeing is believing,' he rejoined. 'That was no clockwork doll Laura Sadlier dragged into the light, it was warm and living, and passion-dazed.'

'Yes, I was dazed—I told you why!'

'We've been over that scene, honey, and I do declare it's straight out of a Lilian Gish movie—now what the devil was it called? I saw it once at the home of a one-time movie mogul who was hung up on silent screen stars—ah yes, *Broken Blossoms* was the title. I daresay in its day it had the girls weeping all over their boyfriends, but I haven't wept in years.'

'You stopped weeping soon after you got pottytrained,' she retorted.

'Now don't go all stiff and tart, *pedhi mou.*'

'I'm not your child!'

'Fortunate, isn't it?'

His smile was wicked, totally unrepentant as he watched her lift her wine glass. 'Don't throw your wine in my face, Wilda Bird. I had this suit made in Savile Row.'

Wilda looked into his jade-grey eyes and tried desperately to hate him, but it was too late for that ... he had won the battle of making her care for him, but he wasn't going to enjoy the victory of subduing her. Anger ebbed away, taking with it the dangerous words that could shatter joy as stones could break glass.

'You must have been a little monster at times, Damien. I pity your nurse and what she had to endure at your mischievous hands.'

'I wasn't always a bad, bad boy,' he said quizzically.

'Ask Mamoushka. She'll vouch for the fact that I could be quite nice when I liked. She was really something in those days, when Troy and I were small boys. Her hair was long and like soft dark fire, and she'd come to the playroom to see us before going out for the evening, all dressed up in silk or velvet and redolent of some delicious scent, gems at her white throat, her lips like petals when she kissed us goodnight. The *patir* would be with her sometimes, and he'd stand there looking like Mount Rushmont, all dark brows and big nose, smelling of strong cigar smoke, and he'd look at me as if I had no individuality of mine but was part of him—like his arm or his leg. He treated Troy like a baby, but I was the firstborn and my destiny was all planned in advance. I was going to walk in his footsteps and follow wherever he led—only it didn't work out that way! He was the one like Napoleon. He made his plans without taking into account that I was too much like him to be led by the nose!'

When he was in this mood, half-mocking and yet with a shadow in his eyes that seemed to hint at some vital torment he couldn't quite suppress, Wilda couldn't stay distant with him. She had to let a smile touch her lips as she tried to imagine him a boy, playing with trains and toy-pistols in a nursery, looking up at his big dark father and seeing the demand written on that hard Greek face. Helios wouldn't have been a father who joined in the games of his children; toy trains and tin soldiers wouldn't have interested Helios Demonides, and Wilda doubted if he had ever taken his little sons to Disneyland.

They had lamb chops with peppered jelly, potatoes baked in their jackets, and tiny green peas. It was delicious, followed by hot sweet cherries and thick cream, and black Greek coffee. Not for a long time had a meal tasted so good to Wilda and they lingered over it, while Damien talked some more about his boyhood and then began to ask questions about her father.

For a long time she had been reluctant to talk about the father she had so much loved, but when Damien suddenly lit a cigarette she felt a nerve of panic flutter in her throat. 'You smoke too much,' she found herself saying. 'It isn't good for you, you must know that. It can kill in a very dreadful way.'

He regarded the cigarette in his hand. 'I guess we've all got to die some time,' he said carelessly.

'But not that way! That's the way my father died, of lung cancer!' Her voice thickened and she cleared it, nervously moving her coffee cup about in the saucer. 'I loved him terribly and I had to watch him slowly disintegrate from a wonderful, vital man into a mere wreck, so weak at the end that he couldn't raise his head from the pillow. It broke my heart—which isn't made of porcelain.'

Damien sat looking at her in a protracted silence, and then with a sudden savage movement he ground out his cigarette in the ashtray. 'I'm sorry, Wilda. I didn't know. It must have been a most unhappy time for you.'

'Hardly bearable,' she admitted. 'We were very close. He and my mother weren't all that compatible, for she didn't share his interest in the making of music, which I did. I travelled about with him and we met some very interesting people; he took me to New Orleans and I loved it there, and then in Paris——' Her fingers gripped her gold necklace. 'He collapsed there and we had to return home to London, and not long afterwards he began to fail. He used to play the saxophone and he even made one or two recordings—I have a lovely one of him playing *Ebb Tide*. His kind of music may not have been classical, but it was very evocative, and that was why I became a singer of songs after he—died.'

She swallowed the painful lump that had come into her throat. And then when she met Damien's eyes she found them as brilliantly hard as jade gems, and the bones of his face seemed to thrust against the tanned skin; he even seemed to have paled a little, for his jaw seemed the colour of iron.

'Was there no one at all who could have stopped you from going alone to a place like Monte Carlo, where you were bound to get drawn into the wrong kind of company?'

Wilda flinched, for like the twisting, lashing tail of a cyclone they always seemed to get back to this point, mounting together into a kind of climax of pain. 'It's depressing, talking about the past—can't we forget the past?' She looked about her, seeking the direction of the dance terrace, where the music was playing. 'Can't we go out there—I suddenly feel rather warm?'

'Of course.' He rose at once and came round to withdraw her chair as she rose to her feet. He took her by the elbow and she quivered at his touch before she could stop herself. 'Do you usually shiver when you're warm, child?' he asked.

'I—it was talking about my father. Nice people shouldn't have to suffer so when they die.'

'No,' he agreed. 'My *patir* fell like a felled log one day in his office, in the middle of checking some accounts. There's no justice, is there?'

'Oh, don't talk like that, Damien!' she begged. 'He wasn't that bad—lots of men expect a son to be their

74

heir apparent. He was a Greek, after all. You come of a dominant race, don't you?'

'I guess I do,' he drawled, and as they reached the terrace he drew her into his arms and she felt him enclose her waist and pull her against his body. 'Wonders will never cease, eh? An orchestra that actually plays civilised music.'

'Yes——' Her heart was beating so she could feel it, and in order to escape Damien's eyes when he glanced down at her, she looked across at the orchestra, its members in cream tuxedos playing among tall potted palms and cascading primavera. She gasped and couldn't believe her eyes, for it was as if talking of the past had resurrected an old friend she had not seen in years. He wasn't playing an instrument but was out front with a baton in his hand, and there was no mistaking his thick, flame-coloured hair and the slanting brown eyes framed in rimless spectacles when he turned to smile at the circling couples, for whom his band was playing *Moonlight Becomes You*.

Kenny ... her kind, gracious friend from the days when life had been a holiday and there had been music from dawn to midnight. Kenny ... who had asked her to marry him and had been too shy to persist in his proposal, which she might have accepted from sheer loneliness.

Suddenly, as she and Damien danced nearer to the orchestra, those brown eyes were staring at her through the rimless spectacles, their pupils pinpoints of sheer amazement and recognition. He mouthed her name to himself, she saw his lips move, and the baton made a false beat which luckily his musicians didn't follow. So Kenny had his own band, as he had always said he would have, certain that pop groups would one day lose their infantile appeal and people would want again to listen to the kind of music that invited romance to the party.

'Who are you staring at?' Damien's voice cut in on her thoughts, and his gaze flashed to the orchestra, to that tuxedoed figure who was staring back at Wilda.

'I—I used to know him,' she said, and there was a warm pleasure in her voice, an awareness that Damien's black brows had merged almost into a scowl of displeasure.

'Sure,' he said, 'they must be dotted about all over the place, men you got to know when you were a free-lance *chanteuse*. It must have been quite a frenetic life, I don't know how you gave it up to become a mother's help.'

His hard words struck through Wilda's delight in seeing someone who had always been kind to her, and she glanced up at Damien's face in an alarmed way. His hand was pressing into her waist in a painful way, and there on his mouth, distorting the fine scrolling of his lips, was an open sneer.

'Oh, God!' The exclamation came from her involuntarily as she realised what he was thinking. 'That's Kenny Devine and he was a friend of my father's. I haven't seen him in a long time—please, don't class him with—with——'

'Sadlier?' Damien inquired, his voice a silken thread of insolence. 'I grant you this one is slightly younger and rather more presentable, but men don't want you for a friend, honey. Do you really imagine you stir avuncular feelings in any normal, fully equipped male?'

'For heaven's sake, Damien——' Suddenly the joy of being close to him on a dance floor had turned cold inside her ... she wanted to break away from him and go running across the floor to Kenny, as she had run to him that day she had gone to the hospital and found her father's bed empty and stripped and she had silently screamed her way all down that long, echoing corridor, finding Kenny at the end of it and able to let loose some of her grief in his arms.

Suddenly the music had stopped and Damien was forcibly leading her from the dance terrace, and when she flung a despairing glance back at Kenny he was standing very still and there was a perplexed look on his face. But he didn't move ... he didn't come and help her this time.

What he had done was to trigger Damien into a hell-raising mood, and there was no getting away from his grip on her arm as he led her down a winding stairway to an oval-shaped door with a glass panel let into it. He rapped on it with his free hand and the panel slid open. A man with a foreign face looked at him, nodded, and the next instant opened the door to let them into a long elegantly appointed room with a deep carpet underfoot and a large cocktail bar to one side of it, where men and women were having drinks and smoking while they talked.

'Do you want a drink before we go into the gaming room?' Damien glanced down at her and his eyes were like slithers of steel in his dark face. 'You look—have something, but I'll wring your neck if you ask for tomato juice!'

'I—I really don't want anything—except to go home——'

'Don't you want to go running to the good-looking boy-friend?' His jawline was hard and grim. 'I could feel it—actually feel it! You wanted to cut away from

77

me and go running to him! He must have been someone really special!'

'He was,' she said tensely. 'Special and nice—and
never like you! Never arrogant and hurtful, the way
you are!'

'Maybe he doesn't have to carry about in his head the
pretty picture I have to carry in mine.' Damien was
bending down towards her, speaking in a voice for her
ears alone, harsh and grating, his breath a rush of
warmth across her skin. 'You with Sadlier, lying there
with your arms around him! God, I could put my
hands around your lovely throat and choke the breath
off your lips because you kissed that lecher with them
—you, who looked so damnably sweet and faraway
when you sang to that guitar, the light in your hair
the way it catches in a child's. Pure, somehow, shining
among a lot of effete and reckless pleasure-seekers, the
so-called jet set! That was the unforgivable part of it,
finding out you were just like them—dross instead of
gold!'

He forced her to the bar and ordered a gin and a
vodka. Wilda sat there on the bar stool and knew it was
useless to try and get away from him. In this mood he
was capable of anything, and the violence smouldering
in him made her feel a little faint. She was glad of the
drink, for it revived her, and she was a little more
composed when they entered the other room that was
alive with the sound of the roulette wheels, the placing
of counters, and the hard little balls as they spun and
bounced and came to settle on the red or the black.

Damien exchanged a wad of notes for a small stack
of counters and they went to the *chemin-de-fer* table
and he played silently for half an hour, piling up more
counters on the green baize, until he suddenly turned

to her and said: 'Want to have a go on the roulette wheel?'

'I can't afford it,' she said, and still felt slightly startled at the way he had played so recklessly and yet had won what she sensed must be a lot of money—more money than she earned in six months!

'I can,' he rejoined. 'Come on.'

'I shall lose it for you,' she protested. 'Cash in what you have and let's go——'

'Not yet. You like pin money, don't you? My mother doesn't pay you so much that you can afford to throw my offer back in my face.'

He took her to the next table and pressed six of the counters into her hand; each one, she knew, represented a lot of dollars, and her hand was shaking as she laid one of them down on the black ... maybe because her evening had turned so dark and whenever she looked at Damien his brows seemed to cast shadows over his face.

The wheel spun, the ball jumped back and forth, and when the wheel rested the ball was indicating that the black had won. Wilda couldn't believe her eyes, and she gave Damien a wondering look. He didn't smile but indicated with a flick of his hand that she leave her winnings where they were. She did so and once again the ball fell upon the black, and her heart gave a funny little trip. It was somehow exhilarating to win, and yet it was also a little frightening.

'Leave them there,' Damien ordered, when she would have reached for the counters. 'Let them run a third time, then we'll go.'

But on that third spin of the wheel Wilda lost, but Damien didn't suggest they remain to recoup her losses. They went to the grilled counter and he cashed the remaining counters, and as they made their way from the gaming room he took hold of her silver bag, opened it and pushed inside several notes of a big denomination. 'Pin money,' he drawled. 'Buy yourself an evening wrap for when the old friend calls to date you.' He snapped shut the bag and when he handed it to her, his smile was at the edge of his mouth, giving his face a cruel look.

'I—I don't want your money, Damien,' she gasped. 'Please, take it back——'

'You'll keep it,' he ordered. 'And one more thing, I gamble on occasion because it amuses me, but I'm not addicted to it. I regard it as fool's gold—come to think of it, there's quite a lot of fool's gold about tonight, isn't there?'

She knew what he meant and there seemed no way of proving to him that she had never lain in Myles Sadlier's arms ... even if she gave him herself as proof, she wasn't so naïve that she didn't know there were other ways of making love with a man, and very often preferred by the genuine *fille de joie*.

Her virginity would prove nothing to Damien ... he carried in his mind a stark image there was no way of erasing, and she had to live with it, or run away from it.

Before leaving the club to drive home she went to the powder-room, needing the respite of being alone for a few minutes. The mirror gave back to her a reflection that was outwardly unimpaired, except for the need of a little lip colouring. It didn't show that inwardly she felt churned up and uncertain what to do with her life. Unless Damien left Moonside before things became too fraught between them, she would have to leave. She didn't want to, but where could any of this lead ...

only to more recrimination and torment. And what if his mother sensed what was going on? She might give Wilda notice to leave, and that would mean that she went without a reference and would find it hard to get a similar kind of job.

And despite seeing Kenny Devine again she didn't want to go back to being a *chanteuse* ... the memories were too bitter, and there were too many men around like Myles Sadlier, to whom a girl's good name meant absolutely nothing. All she had to be thankful for was that at the time of the scandal she had been using the name of Wilda Bird and her father's name had not been mixed up in the sensation of the divorce case. There was every chance that Kenny might not have connected her with anything like that ... she hoped not, for now he knew her to be at Key Laguda he might try to get in touch with her.

She left the powder-room and found Damien awaiting her in the foyer with the velvet cloak over his arm. This time he didn't linger over adjusting it for her, he merely swung it about her shoulders and they walked out of the club in silence.

They had driven about halfway home, not speeding but going fast along the sea-coast highway, when something ran in front of the headlights and Damien swerved, wrenching hard on the wheel in order to avoid what was probably a wild rabbit or a hare, anything that came out at this time of night in order to hunt for food. Wilda was swung against Damien's hard body, and the next moment he had braked against the side of the road, and he sat there with the dashlight casting shadows over his face. They hadn't hit the animal or there would have been a bump beneath the wheels and a possible yelp of distress, but with a sudden groan Damien turned to Wilda and regarded her with a punishing intentness. Then he reached for her, under the folds of the cloak, and she was helpless in those arms that were so strong and determined.

'To hell with it—I want you until it's like being cut open!'

Then she felt the fire and urgency of his lips on hers and the world was oblivion, wiped out by the force of that kiss ... the kiss was eternity and she didn't want to live beyond it to see the old scorn back in his eyes, wounding her as if she were torn open.

Again his mouth, and his hands holding her unbearably close to his hardness. Her arms clung of themselves about his shoulders and her fingers dug into the nape of his neck. When for the moment he had finished with her mouth, she moved her face to the movement of his lips so they could travel freely wherever he wanted them to, across her eyes, down behind her ears, and lower to her throat, bare but for the chain of gold. She could feel his caressing hands and hear his breath dragging hard and deep, and she wanted this, all of this because it stopped him from thinking, stopped him from hurting both of them with his accusing questions that he always answered himself, unable to trust the implausible truth.

She could feel his tense nostrils breathing in the scent of her hair and skin, and the responsive nerves were fluttering in the depth of her body and she knew for the first time in her life what it felt like to want a man. It was an ache, a cry, a longing beyond words, and she was kissing him in return, running her lips over his warm skin and the thrust of the hard bones of his beloved and arrogant face. What did anything matter except that they were together like this and it was warm and real and wonderful?

Then his face was poised above hers, his lips were only a breath away from the desired ravishment of her mouth, and her eyes were open and filled with him, letting him see what she felt, making no demands beyond this time together in the intimacy of his car poised on the road above the mysterious sea.

'You have eyes like the *veilchen*,' he murmured, 'the lovely Alpine violet.'

Then he kissed her again until she felt as if her heart would stop ... and the next instant thrust her away from him, to the far side of the car.

'You go to my head, girl. I could take you, but God help what I'd do to you in the sane light of day.' He started the car and they moved swiftly forward on to the highway. 'I can't trust myself one way or the other with you, Wilda. I want you like hell, but I won't commit myself to you——'

'You can't,' she said quietly. 'We both know you're committed elsewhere.'

'What's that?' He gave her a brief, frowning look.

'That girl—the one you must marry.'

'Ah—yes.'

He looked for a moment disconcerted, and Wilda bit her lip. Perhaps she shouldn't have mentioned the girl, not after the way they had just reacted physically to each other, so lost to what they had felt that there had been no recollection of what was past, or what lay ahead. They had reacted to pure enjoyment of the senses and Wilda knew she would have submitted to him had he demanded it.

He had not, thrusting her away even as the waves of desire swept over them ... a committed Greek, strong in

83

his desires but also strong enough to suppress them even at a critical moment. Even for that Wilda loved him ... yes, she loved him, cruel though he had to be towards her.

She was glad when they turned into the driveway of Moonside, and when the car came to a halt at the front of the house, Wilda slid out and wished him a quiet goodnight. There was no more to be said ... no words that could alleviate the aching sense of loss she felt when she walked away from Damien on trembling legs, praying for him not to follow her or touch her again tonight. Her resistance to him was too terribly weakened and when he held her in his arms it was too easy to forget that he was committed to someone else.

'I won't commit myself to you,' he had said, and his meaning was obvious. He had one involvement and didn't intend to start another, no matter how desirable he had found her response to him. What interpretation had he put upon her response to his kisses ... that she was hungry for a man after all these months of being alone with his mother at Moonside?

Wilda almost dragged herself up the stairs, holding tight to the handrail as if she might topple backwards. It was frightening how emotionally drained she felt, and yet in his arms she had been passionately aware of her body down to the smallest cell, alive to feeling both rapturous and sensuous.

Nothing had ever warned her that love could be this exciting, and at the same time so cruel. Even before she reached the security of her bedroom Wilda felt the soundless slide of tears down her face. Throwing off the velvet cloak, she fell along the length of the bed and allowed herself to sob into the throwover, racked by the loneliness that love brings when it can't be reciprocated.

'We both know you're committed elsewhere,' she had said to Damien, and he hadn't denied that commitment. Added to that she was forever the girl in the St Cyr scandal, and even when he had kissed her as if he wanted to kiss her everywhere she had felt the restrained anger in him, the hint of savagery when he fondled her throat, holding it a moment with his fingers pressing against her skin.

Her weeping done at last, she lay on her back and stared up at the ceiling ... she was never going to get Damien out of her senses, she felt the touch of him still, so strong and vitally alive in every fibre of his body. Her fingers clenched the bedcovers and an aching groan broke from her lips that were still stung by his kisses.

Whatever was she going to do ... had she the strength to walk away from Moonside and not look back?

## CHAPTER FIVE

It was in the dark of the night that the dream usually started, and in a very short while it was a nightmare and Wilda was running endlessly along a white tunnel, screaming for her father, only her screams made no sound and the tunnel had no end, and she just had to make her father see and hear her before he went right away from her:

'Daddy ...' It came at last, a choking cry that always woke her up, hot and tousled from tossing about in her bed, and with the forlorn tears on her cheeks of a small girl left alone in a big house, with no one to comfort her.

Only this time there was someone there; warm, bare arms that pulled her against a solid shoulder and a hand that stroked her tangled hair. 'It's all right,' a deep voice murmured in her ear. 'You were dreaming out loud and I was smoking by the gallery window and I heard you.'

She breathed the cheroot smoke on his skin and when she drew a little away from him she saw the outlines of his face in the milky light of the moon that was coming through her window. Still half dazed by that dream that always seemed so real, her reaction to Damien's closeness was a primitive rush of yearning, followed by the painful awareness that she mustn't give in to what she felt for him. 'Y-you shouldn't be here,' she said, tremulously. 'Not like this—I'll be all right, so please go—go now.'

But he went on holding her and she could feel the strong beating of his heart through the thin silk of her nightdress, feel the heat of his skin because he wore only the pants of his pyjamas. The potent little nerves began to flutter in the pit of her stomach and her hands were touching him before she could stop herself. His skin was supple and firm over the strong bones of his shoulders, and suddenly as weak as water she buried her face against him and her lips tasted the soap he used and a saltiness where he had sweated a little. As he felt her lips on him he gave a sudden deep groan, and the gentleness in his arms was suddenly replaced by an urgency that wouldn't be denied. His weight pinned her to the tumbled bedclothes as he began to make love to her, running his lips back and forth across her soft pulsing throat, his hand pushing aside the fragile straps of her nightdress so he could find her body with his lips.

Wilda gave a soft little moan of longing and all coherent thought had retreated from her mind and all she wanted was to belong completely to Damien ... nothing mattered except that here in the secret night he share a little heaven with her.

She held him to her, murmuring his name as his lips travelled across her creamy flesh ... oh God, it was wonderful and could never be wrong to give in to this glowing, melting sensuality. Nothing in life had ever been so exciting and pleasurable, and she loved him so, her fingers deep in his black hair as he held her in the arc of his strong arm, the tiny muscles contracting in her body as she felt the supple urgency, the ardency for her in his fine body.

She was unafraid of him and deliciously aware of her own feminine power as with a sigh of joy he cradled her to every inch of him, his mouth moving sensuously on hers as his hunger mounted. 'You're adorable,' he whispered. 'I can't wait, Wilda—I want you so, and I'm devilish glad that I don't have to be anxious about hurting you.'

'Hurting me?' she whispered back, too carried away by physical emotion to fully comprehend his meaning. 'Damien darling, you could never hurt me when you're like this with me—oh, I want you!'

'Then it will be perfect,' he exulted. 'No tiresome virginity to worry about!'

She went utterly still ... it was as if every nerve and cell in her throbbing body had suddenly felt a dash of icy water. As swiftly as it had come the overpowering desire was struck dead. Cold reason took its place, and with a sudden jerk that took him completely by surprise Wilda broke free of his embrace and scrambled from the bed, leaving him startled there on one elbow.

'What the hell——?' He stared at her in the moon-glow, clutching her nightdress to her. 'What are you playing at?'

'No more games,' she said huskily. 'Get out of my room, Damien! Leave me alone or I shall yell rape and wake every soul in this house! Do you hear me? You're not getting what you came for after all! Making out you wanted to comfort me for having a frightening dream, but all the time—oh, you're good at it, Damien, a real expert who could make an angel respond to you. You have a marvellous body and you know how to use it, but you have a cruel tongue as well as you know how to use that! Get out of my room à—and in future leave me well alone!'

He slowly sat up and his eyes narrowed to glinting slits as he thrust the black hair back from his brow. The moonlight played over the width of his shoulders and gleamed in the medal that was half buried in the hair of his chest. He looked like some pagan half-god, and Wilda felt the yearning still there, deep inside her, even as she hated him for what he had said to her ... dragging her out of heaven into cold, harsh reality.

'Is it remotely possible that you're still playing the shy and nervous virgin?' His lips twisted with scorn. 'After that display of ardour, my dear? You wanted me as much as I wanted you, and you were displaying as much shyness as a little she-cat purring in the dark. Do you take me for a fool, Wilda? Virgins are scared their first time with a lover, but you—as God is my witness I have never held in my arms a woman so warm and vibrant and *real*, with no coy pretences that a man is a brute and a woman his victim. God in heaven, don't you think I know when my lovemaking is wanted and returned? Why do you have to go on playing this stupid game—does it matter? We're a pair of adults who know what we want—come on, Wilda, come back into my arms.'

Wilda took a deep breath, trying not to see the tension in his face, seeing only that twist to his lips. 'Take your arms—your entire body out of my room, Damien!' Her voice had risen and she had to fight a moment for control, afraid of crying in front of him. 'The very sight of you—you called me a she-cat and I could claw at you for the insulting thing you said. I've never in my life let any man touch me or kiss me the way you have tonight. I wanted to give myself to you so much, I longed to be taught by you all the sweet joys of being with a man, but right there in the middle of what was heavenly you had to go and dredge up what you think of as my murky past. Oh God, what do I do, Damien, to convince you that I've never had a man? Do I take a truth drug in order to prove that only your lips and hands have ever touched me so intimately?'

Silence dragged between them, and then he arose from the bed and turning away from her slid his muscular legs into his pants and settled the black silk against his waist. 'I don't know what I believe any more, Wilda, but there's one thing for sure, you're as capable of being cruel to me as I am of being cruel to you. Next time I touch you, and I promise it will be by accident, don't react with such blood-boiling ardour that a man loses control of himself. If you didn't want me to make complete love to you, then you should have cooled down your ardent responses before I got so much in the mood for it. Do you have any notion of the way I feel right now? I ache to my heels, you little tease! I ache up to the back of my brain! *Kali nikta,* little one, and many thanks!'

He strode from her room with these graphic words, and Wilda was left reeling, her legs giving way as she sank into the warm place on the bed which his body had vacated. She pressed herself into that residue of warmth, but nothing could stop the shivering that took possession of her. She dragged the covers over her and tried to blot from her mind the terrible things they had said to each other.

Heaven and hell, she thought dismally. They were as closely bound as love and hate, with such a fragile skin between them that it could be torn wide open with just a few thoughtless words. She could have ignored what he had said, but at the back of his words there was always the accusation that Myles Sadlier had cheapened her for any other man, and Damien was the offspring of blue-blooded coastal stock, and a tough, proud Greek heritage, somewhat bigoted in its attitude towards women.

It could not be wiped from his mind, even in the midst of passion, that he regarded her as unforgivably soiled by scandal. Suddenly a nausea welled up in her that she had so abandoned herself to a man who basically despised her, and with a retching sound Wilda ran into the bathroom. She leaned weakly against the washbasin and bathed her face with cold water ... what a way, she thought cynically, to end a romantic evening!

Feeling exhausted yet too restless for sleep, Wilda went out on her balcony and took deep breaths of the night air. Above her the sky was filled with the witchery of the moon, a night made for love which had turned to hate. The vivid images moved through her mind as if on a silent screen, the kisses and the passion suddenly joyless ... the caressing ripples of delight replaced by waves of depression.

Her hands clenched the iron handrail of the balcony ... the eternal irony of love was that no matter how physically close you could get to the loved one, you could never know exactly what that person was feeling and thinking. Those thoughts and feelings had to be expressed in words, and Wilda felt sure she could never forgive Damien for revealing in words what he had been thinking while he kissed her mouth with such savage tenderness, and touched her body with such adoring hands. At the very moment when they would have found ultimate joy together he had said that awful, cheapening thing, and Wilda shuddered as she remembered the sudden death of joy right there inside her body, as if he had impaled her on a sharp dagger.

Again the question had to be faced about her future at Moonside. Damien was the son of the house and he had the right to stay here as long as he wished, and while he stayed there would be no cessation for her from this torment of heart, and body. Each time she saw him, each time they were obliged to be polite in front of his mother, both of them would be aware of that scene in her bedroom. It couldn't be forgotten very easily that even without the ultimate intimacy they had behaved with an abandonment which brought a burning flush to Wilda's face. She had caressed and kissed him with equal hunger, loving the supple feel of his skin, the hard closeness of his warm body, the lingering pressure of his lips on her eager mouth.

Her response to him had been ardent, and he had taken it for the expertise of a girl who had made love with other men, yet the irony of it was that only

Kenny Devine had ever kissed her, and so shyly that she had hardly felt anything, least of all those maddening, sensuous ripples of elysium which Damien released in her body so that untutored as she was she knew instinctively how to react to his lips, parting her own so he could kiss her properly; finding the most sentient areas of his body with loving hands that needed no guidance.

Even to think of those moments in Damien's arms was to feel again the exultation, the voluptuous sweetness, the felicity and bliss attainable with a man who was loved ...

Loved? Wilda drew a deep sigh and didn't know any more if what she felt was just a physical infatuation; a need which had nothing at all to do with the basic tenderness of loving someone. Perhaps loneliness and her own femininity had combined to make her want Damien without there being any real love in it. She had never been in love before and might be confusing a desire for his body with a cherishing need for his heart. She doubted if he had a heart in the romantic sense of the word; what pumped away inside that superb frame of his was just another well-constructed engine like the one that ran his car so smoothly. It served to keep him active and able to enjoy his pleasures without getting involved emotionally.

Wilda wished desperately that she could truly hate him, but he had got under her skin and the very thought of him made a palpitation go all through her. He was unbearably exciting, and the sooner she got away from him the better, otherwise there would come another time when she would be unable to resist him, and another time when she would be torn in her deepest feelings by his callous disbelief in her integrity.

In the morning ... yes, the very next day she would hand in her notice to Charmides and make the excuse that she was homesick for England. And with this resolve in mind Wilda returned to her bed and after straightening the covers she fell sleepily inside them and fell into a dreamless sleep.

Unhappily for Wilda's resolve about handing in her notice to quit, the morning brought Inez to her room with the announcement that Madame was feeling ill and would Wilda go to her at once.

Charmides lay moaning in her bed, clutching her stomach and wailing that the room was going round in circles and she felt as if she was going to die. Wilda glanced quizzically at the empty chocolate box on the bedside table, accompanied by spilled ash and a number of well-smoked stubs, including a couple from the finger-sized cigars Charmides was fond of.

'Do you want me to call Dr Martinson?' Wilda asked, not unsympathetically. Her employer was self-indulgent, but at the root of it was a lingering un-happiness from her marriage to a man who had given the most vital part of himself to his shipping business. The very books and films that Charmides enjoyed were an indication that she was warmly romantic, but her husband had been a cool and calculating tycoon, wrapped up in building his own private empire, and when his sons were still just boys he had sent them away to boarding schools, where they had grown self-assured and independent and able to tackle life on their own terms. After the death of Helios his wife had gradually lost interest in the outside world and had become more and more of a housebound recluse, living a life of empty luxury.

Wilda, gripped by sudden compassion, leaned over and felt Charmides' forehead. It was rather hot and there was a hectic flush in her cheeks undue to her usual application of rosy rouge.

'I think I'll call your doctor,' Wilda said, feeling a little jolt of alarm. 'Whereabouts is the pain in your stomach, madame?'

Charmides gave a self-pitying moan and indicated her left side, and then with a confused shake of her head her right side, just beneath her navel. Wilda gently pressed the area and her employer's moan became a sudden yelp. 'It's so sore—oh, what's wrong with me? I do hate being ill, and yet I have to suffer like this!'

Wilda didn't need to ask if Charmides had ever had her appendix removed because there was no visible scarring on her plump white body, and with a set to her jaw she turned to the onyx and ivory telephone and dialled the private number of Dr Martinson, for he wouldn't be at his office this early in the day.

'What's wrong with me, Wilda?' her employer demanded, her flushed features twitching with pain. 'I did eat rather a lot of chocolates last night, and I also had a glass of pink champagne with my supper—is it a bilious attack?'

'It could be, madame,' Wilda said cautiously, 'but I think it best if your doctor gives you an examination—ah, good morning Dr Martinson, I'm sorry to call you so early, but——' She gave her full attention to the telephone and in a matter of minutes had a promise from the doctor that he would be at Moonside within the next hour. She rang off and set about making Charmides as comfortable as possible, bathing her hot skin and putting her into a fresh nightdress, and turning the silk pillow so the cool part was uppermost.

'I want my boy,' Charmides suddenly said fretfully, causing Wilda's heart to give a thump inside her. Of course, there was no avoiding a confrontation with Damien, not when it came to the possibility that his mother was suffering the onset of appendicitis.

'I'll get Inez to fetch him——'

'No, you go and get him,' Charmides ordered. 'He's just along the gallery and it won't take you a minute or two. Tell him I'm suffering and I need him.'

'Very well, madame.' Bracing her shoulders, Wilda went along the gallery, outwardly cool and composed in her uniform, her hair neatly restrained, but quite unable to control the erratic behaviour of her nerves when she tapped upon his door and it was opened almost at once. Damien stood tall and unsmiling in the framework, clad in tapered dark trousers and an aubergine-coloured shirt in dull silk, open against the brown throat she had kissed with hungry lips.

She felt the colour mounting into her face and it took nearly all her courage to meet his eyes, grey and distant as the arctic sea, a set to his jaw that was iron-hard. The look he gave her actually made her cringe away from him, a thrill of fear running across her skin and showing on her face. She had known that he could look as haughty as the devil, but she hadn't known that it would hurt so much when he gave her that look.

'What do you want, Miss Grayson?' His voice was as cutting as steel.

'Y-your mother isn't very well, Mr Demonides.' She fought the tremor in her voice, but like the one in her legs it wouldn't be fully controlled. 'I've had to telephone her doctor and he'll be here soon to make an examination. She sent me to fetch you—she n-needs you.'

At once his manner altered; a look of anxiety sprang

into his eyes and a muscle jerked beside his mouth. 'Have you any idea what's ailing her?' he asked.

'I think it might be inflammation of her appendix,' Wilda said, being frank with him because he would demand nothing less. 'I can tell she's never had trouble in that region and these things can blow up at any time.'

'And she does rather gorge herself, doesn't she?' He pressed his lips together. 'It isn't just that, an attack of over-eating? Last night she was dipping into cream-centred chocolates as if they were going out of fashion.'

'It could be a bilious attack,' Wilda admitted, 'but I'm not going to commit myself. I'm not a proper nurse, as you know.'

'Do I know what's proper about you?' He moved past Wilda and strode off down the gallery towards his mother's room, leaving Wilda to follow in his wake. That last remark had struck like a whiplash, leaving a stinging reminder of the way they had parted last night. Wilda followed him into Charmides' room, where he was leaning over the bed and making soothing sounds as his mother clutched him by the hands.

'I'm afraid, Damien,' she half-sobbed. 'I can't endure the thought of going into hospital and having all s-sorts of horrid things done to me. You won't let them take me there, will you? Dr Martinson will give me something for the pain and it will go away——'

'*Manoula mou*, you must face up to reality,' he said firmly. 'If your doctor decides that the pain is caused by something acute, then you must have the trouble properly seen to. I shall insist on that, so you might as well know it here and now.'

'Yes, because you're as hard as nails like *he* was. True Greeks, the pair of you. Women aren't anything to you except to provide pleasure and consolation—you have no *tendresse*, and I—I pity that girl even though I can't stand the thought of her! Women need love, don't you know that?'

'You think I don't love you, *manoula mou*?' His tone of voice was softer, on the edge of being husky. 'You know different to that, for being nearly all Greek means that I'm of a race of men who place their mothers in a very special category. Come, you know I care for you even if we do have our conflicts.'

'Do you really and truly care for your poor old mother, even when you tell me I wear too much paint on my face and eat too many goodies?' All at once Charmides raised her arms and drew him down to her, and Wilda felt her own hand curling against her heart as Damien's mother kissed his dark and fascinating face. 'The devil gave you charm as well as some iron in your soul—why can't you give me a daughter-in-law I can respect and admire? Why do you have to get yourself mixed up with a *demi-mondaine*? Did you come across her in one of those gambling places you go to?'

'You could say that,' he drawled. 'Now why don't you try and get a little rest before the doctor arrives? Come, let me settle you down.' With those firm, strong hands that Wilda would never forget he laid his mother back against her pillows and drew the bedcovers carefully around her, then he bent his tall head and laid kisses at either side of her face. 'Everything is going to be all right, little mother. You mustn't be afraid of anything because I shall hold your hand.'

Wilda swayed and clutched the edge of the dressing-table, almost overcome by the tenderness with which he spoke to his mother ... she felt tingling tiny pains in her very bones and felt that her face had gone ashen with a very personal emotion. Oh yes, she was in love with this exciting and complex man, in whom the mixed blood caused cross-currents that could sweep a woman into the dangerous depths of his personality. He was as much a perplexity to his mother as he was to her, and then she heard Charmides say to him:

'I believe if you ever loved a woman beyond reason, Damien, you would do anything for her and she'd be the most blessed of young women. Oh why——?'

'Don't let's get into that argument again, *mamoushka*. Are you still in pain?'

Charmides gave a stricken, eloquent twist of her mouth, and he turned at once to Wilda. 'Is there nothing you can give her for the pain?' he asked curtly.

'I—I mustn't give her anything, Mr Demonides,' Wilda said, pulling herself together. She took a quick look at her wristwatch. 'Dr Martinson should be here very soon and he'll be able to diagnose exactly what is wrong with Madame.'

'You are telling me she has to endure her pain without any kind of relief?' he demanded, and his eyes raked over Wilda's face with a coldness she could hardly bear.

'I—I'm afraid so. An inflammation of the stomach could be caused by a number of things, but if it's——' Wilda broke off, not wishing to add to Charmides' fear and anxiety. 'I prefer not to administer a pain-killer, Mr Demonides, but Madame is your mother and if you feel——'

'No.' He stood frowning darkly, a tall and overpowering figure in his mother's pink and frilly bedroom. 'You aren't a fool and you've worked, so you tell me, in a hospital. She can't even have a cup of tea with plenty of milk in it?'

Wilda shook her head. Oh, didn't he realise? If his mother had appendicitis then the doctor might decide that she needed an immediate operation, and in these cases the sooner the appendix was removed the better chance the patient stood of avoiding any complications.

He stood there, hands thrust into the pockets of his trousers, and abruptly he gave a nod as if he had read her mind. 'You're right, of course, Miss Grayson. Perhaps you would like to go and have a cup of tea yourself? I shall remain with my mother.'

'Very well.' Wilda moved to the door, still feeling that nervous tremor in her legs. At the door she hesitated, and then shot him a half-shy look. 'Perhaps I could bring you some tea or coffee?'

'Tell Inez to bring me a cup of coffee,' he rejoined, and with that he turned his back on her and drew forward a chair so he could sit at his mother's bedside. Wilda swallowed the painful lump in her throat and hastened away, moving down the stairs like an automaton. It seemed as if she would never again in her life know the infinite joy she had come so close to knowing last night, in those arms from which she had dragged herself, wanting not only Damien's passion but his respect as well.

She made tea for herself in the kitchen, while Inez took coffee to Damien, and she had just finished drinking it when Dr Martinson arrived. Wilda explained why she was concerned as they went upstairs together, but when they reached her employer's bedroom she hung back and didn't enter with the doctor. Damien was with his mother, and if the doctor wanted her to be present during his examination he would ask for her.

Wilda went and stood at one of the gallery windows and felt the anxiety playing on her nerves, so that when

Damien approached her it was impossible not to react with an involuntary withdrawal into the window alcove.

'I'm not carrying a whip, so don't keep cringing away from me,' he said, cuttingly. 'The doctor says he will call us when he's completed his examination—he looks impassive, but I suppose that's the usual mask these medicos wear on such occasions.'

Wilda nodded and didn't know what to say to him. Too much had already been put into words between them, and she was so acutely sensitive to his cold, contemptuous attitude that a withdrawn silence seemed her only defence. She couldn't feel angry any more, even though he was making her feel the guilty one. A tease, he had called her, who had led him on and denied him the natural release for his ardour. She hadn't meant it to be that way, but when he had spoken with such a casual assumption that she wasn't virgin, Wilda had reacted with all the outrage of the state of virginity.

Very obviously he was a man who confined his amorous attentions to experienced women, and it hurt Wilda deeply to be classed with their type, who made of love a game for two casual players, who went their separate ways when the kissing was over.

She stood there in the alcove, gazing blindly from the window, and conscious of nothing but the tall figure who stood just a few inches from her tense, uniformed figure. Nothing they had said last night, nothing they had felt could be easily forgotten by either of them ... the flame had sunk to a smoulder, but it was still there and they were both aware of it.

'He's taking his time.' Damien glanced at his watch on its crocodile strap. 'I hope to God he hasn't found something seriously wrong with her. She isn't a young woman any more and all this lazing about and indulging herself with sweet things hasn't done her a lot of good. Couldn't you have seen to it, Miss Grayson, that she ate more moderately? Have you deliberately stood by and watched her eat her way through pounds of candy, and drink her way through bottles of pink champagne? She always loved that particular beverage, but you claim to have some nursing experience so you must be aware of the dangers of over-indulgence.'

'Yes, Mr Demonides.' Wilda felt her pulses racing with the temper she had sworn to herself to suppress. 'I know of them, but I'm not your mother's keeper. I was employed to be her personal maid and companion, but it was never stated that I was to be the custodian of her larder and her cellar. How long do you think I would remain here if I started to dictate to her? It's perfectly obvious that you have never worked for someone but have always been your own boss, otherwise you wouldn't assume that a wage-earner has rights. I am one of the hired help at Moonside, and I depend on what I earn to buy clothes and necessities—which reminds me that I have two hundred dollars to return to you, which you put into my purse last night, and which you must obviously feel you have been cheated out of.'

Her words were followed by a silence that was not only menacing, it was deadly. Under his deep tan Damien seemed to have actually paled, and then with fury seething in his eyes he leaned down to Wilda and he spoke through his teeth. 'Yes,' he said, 'for that price I could get myself a real high-class *fille de joie*, but you're a rank amateur, aren't you? You keep on being a mother's help, my dear. It may not pay so well, but you're less likely to get your neck broken the next time you lead a man on and then turn chicken!'

'I—I didn't lead you on,' she denied hotly. 'Y-you came into my room—I didn't invite you in. You took me in your arms and——'

'And you didn't exactly turn to ice when I kissed you! No, that came later, when you had me all nicely steamed up. You beautiful little fraud, I should have gone ahead and made you earn every one of those dollars—the way you probably earned them with Sadlier! I guess with him the ice-maiden routine didn't work when you switched it on, and he didn't behave the gentleman, as they call it? More fool me, and I'm not usually so foolish, for even in that uniform with your hair swept back in a bun you have a quality of allure that sets a man's pulses on edge, like tiny drums that beat out a battle call to which he responds even as he retreats. The call of Lorelei, beckoning men on into the trap of your pale gold hair and your *veilchen* eyes ... try that on with me another time, Wilda, and I shall forget my upbringing and not bow out of your alluring presence quite so gracefully.'

Wilda could only look at him, too lost for words to be able to fend off the attack he had made on her. How could he believe it of her, that she had taken money from Myles Sadlier ... that she deliberately set out to attract men only to repulse them when they were at their most vulnerable?

'How you must despise me,' she said at last, and suddenly her face contorted and tears filled her eyes before she could fight them off. The deep blue of her eyes trembled through the tears, which fell like acid down over her cheeks, running into the corners of her mouth. Through the blur she could see his grim face, and then quickly she turned aside and brushed angrily at the tears with the heel of her hand.

'How prettily you cry,' he mocked. 'How readily you can turn on the tears so they make those eyes of yours shimmer like violets in the rain. God, yes, you're lovely! You have all the armoury that makes men defenceless, but I'm on to you, little one, and it will be an immeasurable pleasure to disarm you the next time we find ourselves locked in combat.'

'T-there won't be a next time,' she flung at him. 'I'm leaving Moonside and I'm going miles away where I shan't have to run into you ever again. I can't bear it, the way you twist everything so I'm always in the wrong. It was you! You said that unbearable thing to me even as you m-made love to me——'

'What did I say?' His hardness of voice was matched by the hard set to his features; his eyes were cold steel.

'Dear God, don't pretend you've forgotten.' Wilda could have struck him across his mouth, with that twist of contempt at the edge of the lips which had moulded themselves so closely to hers until he wrung from her a soft moan of purest joy ... animal joy, which he could probably wring from any woman.

'Please enlighten me,' he drawled. 'I remember saying things, but my mind wasn't exactly involved, if you take my meaning. Come, what terrible thing did I say that turned your heatwave into a sudden snowstorm?'

'You must know!' she exclaimed. 'Y-you kiss me the way you did, hold me as if I meant something to you, and then expect me not to be hurt when you—you said that cheap, cruel thing about not having to worry because I had no tiresome—that I wasn't——' Wilda couldn't go on, and the abrupt comprehension in his eyes made it unnecessary that she continue to the bitter end.

'What's so terrible about the truth?' he queried. 'No virgin was ever that responsive in a man'e arms——'

'Why?' Her eyes blazed though her lashes were still tear-wet and clustering. 'Do you make a habit of seducing virgins? I should have said you were a man who preferred the liberated type of woman who takes her pleasures as she would take a cocktail snack at a party. Easy come, easy go, with no strings—though I'm forgetting, of course, that one of your involvements did lead to complications. Was she a virgin?'

Damien stared down at Wilda and his eyes had become ignited from hers, looking raw silver in his angry dark face. 'It occurs to me,' he said, grimly, 'that all lovemaking should be carried out in silence, except for the exciting little sounds that orchestrate the procedure. So if I had kept my mouth shut and played your little game of make-believe, I would now have a pleasant memory to look back on instead of a bitter, aching—well, let's call it regret. You are a lovely thing and you have a mouth I could eat, but, by God, don't pretend with me that you're a shy violet waiting to be plucked. I saw you after your initial plucking, honey, and it was a rare and exquisite scene!'

Wilda flinched at every word, backing physically away from him until she was right inside the alcove and pressed up against the window ledge. She felt as if each separate word was a whiplash, striking across her skin and inducing a stinging welt. Nothing in her life had ever hurt so much, that always there had to come between them that nightmare scene at the St Cyr. It poisoned everything they said and felt, and made her life at Moonside impossible to endure.

'Please—no more!' She cried out the words as if she

were being physically attacked. 'As soon as we have Dr Martinson's verdict on your mother I'll pack my belongings and leave right away. I can't stay here! I just haven't the courage for it!'

Damien, with a silent air of menace, followed her into the alcove until he was towering over her. 'If my mother needs you, then you stay here,' he said emphatically. 'This between us is purely physical—or should I use the term impure? We're like this with one another, snarling and spitting like a pair of sand-cats, because last night you went to my head like a bitter-sweet wine and left me with one hell of a hangover. I repeat, Miss Grayson, you aren't leaving this house if my mother still requires you.'

'I can't stay,' Wilda gasped. 'You can't make me——'

'Want to bet?' He stood over her, both arms extended to the window frame so that she was trapped in their unyielding arc. 'No doubt you have a contract with my mother which requires that you give a month's notice before leaving her employ. And no doubt she holds your employment document which permits you to work in America. I can get hold of it any time I wish, and you try finding a job without that document.'

'I—I do believe you're the cruellest man I ever met.' Wilda's eyes were suddenly bleak. 'Anyone who upsets you is really asking for trouble.'

'Quite so,' he agreed. 'I despise your kind of provocateuse.'

'And I despise bullies,' she rejoined. 'You can't keep me here against my will—I'll use that roulette money to get away from you!'

'Just try using it, little one.' His smile was infinitely taunting. 'I shall phone the local sheriff and accuse you of stealing money from me.'

'You—you wouldn't dare!'

'Try me, honey.' His eyes were adamant. 'I'm in the mood for daring anything with regard to you. Two hundred dollars is a lot of cash for a mother's help to have in her possession, and you try convincing anyone that I gave it to you for pin money. They'll laugh at the idea, or take you for a *fille de joie*. Which do you prefer, the tag of thief or scarlet woman?'

'I hate you!' Wilda said, meaning it so much in this moment that it was actually there in her eyes, making them burn like blue flames in the pale gold pallor of her face. 'You're an arrogant bully who must have your own way no matter what the cost to anyone else. How I'd like to see you on your knees and at the mercy of something stronger than yourself. I'd rejoice!'

What his reply might have been Wilda never knew, for at that precise moment Dr Martinson came along the gallery and at the sound of his footfalls Damien swung away from her and confronted the doctor. 'How is my mother?' he asked. 'I hope you haven't found anything seriously amiss with her?'

'I have just this minute telephoned for an ambulance,' Dr Martinson replied, in a sympathetic tone of voice. 'Madame Demonides has an inflamed appendix, as Miss Grayson suspected, and the sooner we get her into hospital the better for her. It could rupture at any time, for she is considerably overweight and that doesn't help, but there is no need for undue alarm. Her heart is sound and the operation is a comparatively simple one.'

The doctor glanced at Wilda, who had now emerged from the alcove and was looking as composed as her shaken nerves would allow. The bleak look in her eyes could only be mistaken for anxiety regarding Charmides, and Dr Martinson said in a kindly voice: 'I'm glad you were so prompt in phoning me, Miss Grayson, and that you didn't mistake those symptoms for a stomach upset. I understand Madame Demonides had rather a heavy supper last night, and she also ate a considerable quantity of candy—I'm afraid after this flare-up she's going to have to restrict her eating habits, and I hope you'll see to it that she keeps to the diet I shall prescribe for her.'

'Yes, doctor.' This was no time for Wilda to say that she intended to leave Moonside just as soon as Charmides was well again. She watched Damien go striding into his mother's bedroom ... he would go with her in the ambulance to the hospital, holding her hand as he had promised, but when he returned home, Wilda would have to share this big house with him.

She didn't dare to contemplate the immediate future ... seeing him each day, knowing he was only a few doors away from her each night. What would she do next time she had her nightmare and woke to find herself in his arms?

CHAPTER SIX

FATE was such a powerful force, thought Wilda; it had swung her from Monte Carlo to the Florida Keys and then made it impossible for her to leave because a woman had undergone surgery and was slowly recovering her health and strength in the tall white hospital that was one of the proud possessions of Key Laguda.

The operation had been successfully carried out five days ago and there had been no complications. Wilda was thankful for that, but there was little else for her to take pleasure in, for even when she came to the beach she brought with her the constant edginess of the conflict smouldering between Damien and herself. Their cool politeness, their long silences were always on the edge of a sudden eruption, and the atmosphere was wearing Wilda to a shadow. She had lost her appetite and her face looked fine-boned and haunted.

If only he would let her go! But he seemed to take a perverse pleasure in making sure she stayed. He had charge of the key to the desk in which Charmides kept private and important documents, and Wilda's work permit was among them, contained in an envelope with her passport and her health certificate. It had seemed quite reasonable at the time to let Charmides keep them in her desk, where they would be secure, but Wilda was cursing herself for not looking ahead; for not making allowance for the fact that she might yet again meet a man from whom she would wish to flee.

Whenever Damien was absent from Moonside, she thought seriously about breaking the lock of her employer's desk, a pretty rosewood one that stood between the windows of the sitting-room adjoining her bedroom. But such an action constituted a crime and Wilda shrank from injuring the principles which her father had taught her. But her distress was so acute at times that she almost believed she could break into the pretty desk and take what was hers, and one afternoon she had approached it with a hammer she had found in the cellar, but her resolve fled away when she tried to bring that hammer down on the lock. She shrank away from a mental image of the shattered rosewood ... the grim and dangerous look that would come over Damien's face when he found the desk had been broken into.

Wilda had suffered through one scandal and couldn't face another, and she believed that Damien was ruthless enough to report her to the police. His kind of integrity was nail-hard, and he found it so unforgivable that she had got under his skin ... perhaps like a jigger worm that delved deeper each time he tried to dig her out of himself. It would give him satisfaction, she told herself, to see her driven off in the sheriff's car.

Damn him! She pounded the firm, sunlit sand where she lay. If only she could dig him out of her thoughts ... her innermost self, but he wouldn't be dislodged and the torment of him was always there, right inside her.

How could the poets have written so sentimentally of love when it was really the most unreasonable emotion anyone could suffer! It had a wayward will of its own and took not the slightest heed of cruel remarks and hateful behaviour; it could still turn her heart when Damien strolled into a room, or suddenly caught her gaze across the dining-table.

Wilda yearned to get away from this hard, complex man, but until his mother was well and truly on the mend she had to stay at Moonside; she couldn't yet ask Charmides to release her, not while she lay in hospital.

Wilda closed her eyes and tried to relax. The sand was like warm plush beneath her body and she lay listening to the seducing, gravelly whisper of the surf, so insistent in its rhythm as it surged to the sands and then withdrew, again and again.

She felt rather than saw the shadow that suddenly fell over her reclining body and she tensed in her every nerve. Her heart pounded, and then a voice said: 'You are Wilda, aren't you? Wilda, the daughter of

Jeff Grayson, who I knew a few years back?'

Kenny? Her eyes flew open and she sat up, and the next instant was on her feet, a slim, eager figure in her ink-blue swimsuit with insets of white. Their hands reached and clung, and the sun seemed to strike tiny flames from his auburn hair. He wore sun-glasses, and ivory slacks with a sea-island cotton shirt. He looked fit and so dearly familiar, even though they hadn't seen each other for such a long time.

'Wilda.' He spoke her name wonderingly. 'I could hardly believe my eyes when I saw you at the Dinarzade last week—it had to be you! No other girl ever had hair the exact colour of champagne, or those big blue eyes that seem to—to——' Kenny broke off, swallowing hard. 'That chap you were with, is he your husband? I saw the way he was holding on to you, and he glowered at me as if he meant to come across and shake me by the scruff of the neck. He's foreign, eh? Someone you met during your singing tour?'

'No,' she shook her head and had to hold on tight to Kenny's hands for she suddenly felt unsteady. 'Damien isn't my—husband. I work here as companion to his mother. In that house just above the beach.'

Kenny cast a look at it, and then glanced down at their intertwined hands. 'Of course, no ring.' He gave a slightly husky laugh. 'What a relief, but from the chap's manner—you seemed rather afraid of him. I wanted to come across and speak to you, but he took you away from the terrace and his attitude was so—is he someone special, Wilda? Oh lord, how often I've longed to see you again, and now——'

'No.' She said it emphatically. 'He isn't anyone special, and that arrogant manner of his—well, that's how he is. These people I work for are part Greek and

I've been here at Key Laguda for almost a year.'

'Then you aren't singing any more?' Kenny gave her a perplexed look. 'You had an attractive way with a song, Wilda. Why did you give it up? I always thought you could land a recording contract.'

'I—I didn't care for the life,' she said evasively. Kenny obviously knew nothing about the *débâcle* at Monte Carlo, and she wasn't going to enlighten him until they had cemented their friendship again. She had learned the hard way from Damien that you could never be sure how a man was going to react to the trouble a girl alone could get into, condemning her as guilty even if she went on crying her innocence while having each separate toenail torn out.

She gave a little shudder and suddenly there were tears in her eyes. 'Oh, Kenny, you can't imagine how glad I am to see you, but how did you come to find me? How did you know I'd be here at Moonside?'

'Pure accident—or the beckoning finger of fate. I had a few hours to myself from the band and decided to take a drive along the seacoast road. I spotted this beach and the sands looked so inviting, and I decided to risk its being a private area. Then as I came round from that fringe of rocks I saw a girl stretched out on a tangerine rug, her hair flowing in the sunlight like spilled champagne. Only one girl I ever knew had hair like that—if possible, Wilda, you're even more charming than I recall. A real enchantress, if I may say so? Your father would have been proud of the woman you've grown into.'

'I—I hope you're right, Kenny,' she murmured. 'I've tried to live up to the principles he taught me, but life —life isn't always easy, is it?'

'No, sweetheart.' He drew her hands against the

front of his patterned shirt and she felt his reassuring warmth, and also realised that he had grown less shy with women and was far more confident with her.

'Kenny, you have a great band,' she said admiringly. 'It felt so good being able to dance to some of the melodies that used to be written. You always said you'd get your own boys together and make that kind of music again. My father would have been proud of you.'

'Jeff was a broth of a boy,' Kenny said nostalgically. 'I often think about the good times the three of us had together—strange the way things work out. I never dreamed when I signed to play at the Club Dinarzade that I'd see you dancing there. This Greek chap, I imagine he's likely to boot me off his private property if he should see me talking to you? Are you part of his property, Wilda? These days, as we all know, people don't always bother to tie the legal knots in order to belong to one another, and I don't want to trespass if you belong to him in any way. Not only because he looks as if he swings a hard punch, but because I respect you, and if he's your choice, then I'm going to wish you a fond farewell and say thanks for the memories.'

'Is that the way it looked, Kenny?' Her deep blue eyes brooded on his good-looking face, with the nice regular features and the faunish eyes that were half-concealed behind the smoked lenses of his sunglasses. With his dark-flame hair and his slender, almost dapper appearance he couldn't have been more of a contrast to Damien, whose black hair was often rough from the sea-salt, and who liked to wear his shirts unbuttoned to his belt. When he did dress up he had a commanding air, his tailored suits becoming part of his tall, supple frame. In everything he was the governing factor, and his clothes, whether casual or formal, were there to suit his purpose and not to present him in the best possible light to anyone observing him. In all fairness, Wilda had to admit that Damien Demonides was as unselfconscious as the panther she had admired that long-gone sunny day at Regent's Park with her father—and yes, Kenny had been there with them! And how he had laughed when she refused to enter the insect house in case one of the tarantulas got loose.

When she shivered, Kenny gave her a concerned look.

'Someone trod on my gravestone,' she said, and his hands tightened protectively on hers. 'There are times when I miss Daddy so much that I ache in my heart, Kenny. He was a lovely man, wasn't he? Not so long ago I read a book about Scott Fitzgerald, and I was astonished by his physical resemblance to Daddy. Both so fair and blue-eyed, and somehow shining, like knights of chivalry; and they both died so young, with so much left unaccomplished.'

There followed a little regretful silence, and then Kenny spoke with a firmness she had not detected in him in the old days. 'Tell me about the Greek,' he insisted.

Wilda searched his face and saw jealousy there, and the nerves tightened in her midriff, like tiny strings tugging at her. 'He's the son of my employer, as I told you, Kenny.' She paused and took a firm grasp on the lie that must be made to sound like the truth. 'He's nothing to me, and I'm certainly less than nothing to him.'

'Forgive me for saying this, Wilda, but it didn't look that way on the club terrace.' Kenny's dark red brows were drawn together above the rims of his sunglasses.

'He was holding you as if you belonged to him and nobody else in the world. He was—possessing you, to my music!'

'No, Kenny——'

'Yes, Wilda. I've been too long in this business and stood on too many rostrums and watched many couples dance together. Some are frankly bored as they circle the floor, others are pleasantly occupied, and some even smooch, but that tall Greek was holding you as Paris must have held the lovely Helen of Troy! You say you mean nothing to him—I'd say you meant a hell of a lot to him.'

'It just isn't true, you've got to believe me.' There was pain in her voice, and her eyes were shadowed by memories Kenny couldn't share. Damien had a natural air of command with a woman which a shy man would mistake for possessiveness; only she could know the depth of Damien's contempt for her, the girl he thought of as Myles Sadlier's *fille de joie*. 'I only stay on at Moonside to suit Madame Demonides, who happens to be rather ill at the present time. When she's fit again I shall be moving on.'

'That evening at the club,' Kenny murmured, 'I must admit I got the impression that you were afraid of the man—does his mother know that he bullies you? Or is she the type of doting mother who condones his behaviour?'

'Madame isn't completely unaware that he's a—a bit of a devil.' Wilda bit her lip. 'As soon as possible I shall quit Moonside, and I may return to England. Does that, Kenny, sound like the plan of a girl who has anyone here in Florida who cares—really cares about her? Sometimes I feel as if no one has cared since Daddy went out of my life, and it was like a light going out and leaving shadows. I—I get so lonely!'

'Poor little girl.' Kenny drew her suddenly close to him and she was glad to rest there, with her head against his shoulder. It was the first time in a long while that she had felt she could trust a man, and on impulse she put her arms around him and lifted herself on her bare toes in the sand so she could kiss him. He was tense for a moment, and then with a ragged little sigh he returned her kiss, pressing his lips to her slightly trembling mouth.

And right in the midst of that sweet reunion with Kenny there came a note of crushing discord that paralysed Wilda so that her lips seemed unable to withdraw from Kenny's. 'What a delightful picture of mutual bliss,' drawled a voice with insolence in it. 'A real image of passion under the palms—no, I beg of you both, don't let me disturb you, you just go ahead and enjoy yourselves.'

It was the sheer insolence that Wilda couldn't stand, and obedient to the sarcasm she held on to Kenny and sustained their kissing position for several more moments. To hell with Damien! Let him watch and fume!

It was Kenny who drew away, and instantly she flung Damien a reckless look, tossing back the soft mane of her sun-touched hair from her flushed face. He returned her look by quirking a black eyebrow, and his eyes were still as lake water on a hot day. He seemed very sure of himself as he stood with his hands in the pockets of his grey trousers, the jacket removed from his dark-wine shirt with white buttons.

'Won't you introduce me to your—friend?' He moved his gaze to Kenny. 'Ah yes, I recognise you, you're the band-leader, aren't you, from the Club

Dinarzade? I recall that Wilda told me you were old acquaintances.'

Forcing herself to be cool about it, Wilda introduced the two men formally, and a little to her surprise Damien moved forward so that he could offer Kenny his hand. There was something in the gesture she couldn't quite fathom ... and then it struck her that he was saying without words that he was fully aware of her power to lead men on and he didn't blame Kenny for kissing her.

Now she was fuming and could have struck that little twist of a smile from his mouth as he shook hands with Kenny, looking very dark and tanned in contrast to the band-leader, everything about him suggesting a vigour the other man couldn't compete with. They were of a similar age, and yet he made Kenny look callow in his sea-island cotton shirt, with his auburn hair as smooth as fox fur.

'What do you think of Florida, Mr Devine?' he asked.

'It's a nice place,' Kenny replied, and he looked slightly awkward, as if he still didn't believe what she had insisted was true, that she and Damien meant nothing to each other. She wondered if Kenny had expected Damien to swing a punch at him ... oh, why hadn't it occurred to her that he would be back from town around this time in the afternoon? He usually lunched there after visiting his mother at the hospital, and there was every likelihood that he had spotted Kenny's car at the roadside and his reflexes were always on the alert.

'Come to the house and have a drink.' Damien invited. 'Today has been quite a sizzler, hasn't it: We could be in for a squall later on, fair weather is often followed by storm, eh?'

Kenny nodded. 'I understand the Key storms are really terrifying when they blow up, and I imagine as you live right on the edge of the sea, it must be a spectacular sight.'

'Awe-inspiring,' Damien drawled. 'The waves tower as high as our verandas and they crash about like sea demons let loose, added to which there's the noise. These houses along the coast are built with storm cellars, of course, but it's too good a spectacle to miss.'

'You mean you watch it?' Kenny glanced at the sea, which at the moment was limpid and sparkling blue. It seemed impossible that fury could launch itself from that seabed, but there had been such a storm soon after Wilda had come to work at Moonside and upon that occasion Charmides had insisted on going down to the cellar, where a room was comfortably furnished for such occasions, complete with a small cocktail bar, card tables and shelves of books. While the squall had raged, Wilda had been confined with her employer underground, but when Damien spoke of those towering waves and that daemonic fury, she felt the excitement stir inside her and had a feeling she would want to watch from the veranda next time a squall struck the waters of Key Laguda.

'Shall we go and have that drink?' Damien inquired.

'Thanks all the same, but I have to be getting back to the club.' Kenny, usually a sociable person, was looking at Damien with an unsmiling face. Then he glanced at Wilda and his facial muscles relaxed. 'Shall I be seeing you, Wilda? Maybe you could come into town and lunch with me?'

'You can bank on it,' she assured him warmly. 'I'll phone you at the club, shall I?'

'Grand!' He stepped towards her, then halted. 'I'm glad we've met up again, Wilda. It will be a pleasure to talk about old times, won't it?'

She nodded and again she took the initiative, and stepping up to him raised herself on her toes and kissed his cheek. 'Goodbye for now!'

''Bye!' He inclined his head towards Damien and walked away, and when he was out of sight Wilda braced herself and turned to where Damien had been standing. But he moved away to the edge of the ocean and his sandalled feet were in the surf and he gazed broodingly across the water.

'I came to tell you,' he said, 'that my mother has had a slight relapse and isn't quite so well as she was. I thought you might drive in with me this evening and pay her a visit.'

'Oh—I'm sorry she isn't so well.' Wilda spoke sincerely. 'If you think Madame would like to see me, then I'll certainly visit her. I can arrange for a cab to take me——'

'The hell you can!' He swung towards her and his face was suddenly dark with temper. 'I've invited you to go with me, and you can cut out being clever with me just because an old boy-friend has turned up and you're feeling skittish. Have the pair of you been catching up on all the little happenings since you last met, not to mention the big ones?'

The quick-tempered words sprang to Wilda's lips, but just as swiftly she bit them back. She could sense that he was upset about his mother, concerned because he was up against a situation he couldn't handle for himself. Wilda knew he had sent a wire to his brother Troy on the day their mother had gone into hospital, but Troy's secretary had wired back that he was in Athens on business and couldn't be located, but as soon as possible they would inform him that he was urgently wanted in Florida. So far there had been no word from him to say he was on his way to Key Laguda, which meant that Damien had no one close to him to share his anxiety.

Wilda felt sympathetic where his mother was concerned, but she wasn't in a position to show it except in the polite way of an employee. And now when he did ask her to share a visit with him, she reacted with a show of foolish pride and made him lose his temper ... oh, why had she done it, implying that a public cab was preferable to the privacy of his car? Now she had triggered his temper and made him sarcastic about Kenny.

'I—I've always been fond of Kenny,' she said. 'He's probably the nicest man I know, and we share good memories of my father. He doesn't know what happened in Monte Carlo, but I shall get around to telling him——'

'I shouldn't,' Damien cut in, 'not if you want to keep that adoring look on his clean-cut face. He obviously regards you as Miss Muffet and Goody Two-Shoes all rolled into one, and it would be a pity to disillusion such a nice fellow.'

'The truth can't disillusion him,' she protested. 'Kenny isn't a cynic like you.'

'No, he's a band-leader, and they're notorious for their schmaltzy attitude. I guess it's all that romantic music played on moonlit terraces.'

'A little schmaltz is better than your worldly derision of—of simple things.' Her cheeks stung when she looked at him, from a combination of salt in the air and sarcasm in his eyes. 'I'm glad Kenny's the way he is, nice and uncomplicated. He may not have your charisma, Mr Demonides, but along with it you're a

119

master of contempt. When I come to think of it, what happened to me at Monte Carlo is really none of your business, so I don't know why you let it annoy you so much.'

'Don't be so sure that nice, uncomplicated Kenny won't be—annoyed. Just for the record, Wilda Bird, how did you get involved with Sadlier in the first place? Did he offer you stardom in movies and a mansion at Bel Air?'

'No.' Her eyes burned with resentment of Damien's question, and the bitter memory of what her young loneliness had led to when she had allowed Myles Sadlier to take her horseback riding, and had let him teach her how to handle his sports car. She had believed in his sympathy because he was a paternal age and had crinkly blue eyes. She had been too naïve to realise that malign thoughts could be lurking behind a bland smile. She had walked into the trap he had set for her like the proverbial fly, and she had woken up with her wings badly scorched.

She shivered in retrospect at the way she had been dragged by her hair in front of her accusers—like some Biblical adulteress—and it seemed as if the stones would never stop bruising her while she remained in the vicinity of this tall, dark man who went on accusing her. This man she desired with her body and disliked with her mind!

She was constantly aware of the struggle going on within her, so intricate was the web in which they were tangled. Driven by needs they couldn't put into words. Possessed by demons they were at times beyond controlling.

Love, the heaven of immeasurable promise, was not

part of what they felt ... certainly no part of his feelings with regard to her!

She felt his eyes raking over her slenderness in the blue and white swimsuit, and his look made her mouth go dry. No! She felt that electrifying tingle over her skin. Oh no! She backed away from him, knowing too well that when he touched her, she lost all sense of reason and wanted to be his with an abandon that was shocking and primitive, so that nothing on earth mattered except that she become part of him and experience the very ultimate in sensual fulfilment. It was a madness she had to fight ... he didn't love her and she had resolved that he wouldn't take her and make of her just another conquest to add to his collection.

'Don't touch me,' she breathed, 'I couldn't bear it!'

'Would it be too unbearably exciting?' He spoke in a dangerous murmur, reading her eyes with his and watching the rapid rise and fall of her bosom beneath the clinging material of her swimsuit. 'It hadn't occurred to me to touch you, Wilda. I said I wouldn't, except by sheer accident, and I meant it. But I admit you're very exciting in your swimwear. I always think a one-piece suit is more stylish than the erotic but ugly bikini, which conceals nothing and often reveals too much.'

'When you look at me you touch—please stop it!' She had backed all the way beneath the palm trees that provided shade from the sun when it was too pitiless, and she gave a start when her body came into contact with the scaly trunk of one of the trees. She stood there on the defensive, like a creature at bay who was frightened to run because she knew she would be outdistanced, and yet who also knew that she would be unequal in a close fight. She was a slim, pleading figure, bare-limbed, her hair a bright tumbling mass about her deep blue eyes. She felt and looked crucified on the steel of Damien's eyes as he deliberately came up the beach towards her. There was a controlled energy in the way he moved; he was alert, powerful, like the sensual panther. There was a superb aliveness about him, and in the whisper of the surf there was the memory of gravelly whispers against her throat, of hands that moved over her body with a bold strength and promise that tantalised to madness ...

And then she did go mad ... a curdling sound escaped from her throat as something black and hairy leapt on crooked legs from the upper part of the palm tree, its quivering obscene body landing on Wilda's bare shoulder. She screamed shockingly and the next instant Damien was there, having pelted across the beach to her side, and swung his arm so that he knocked the beastly object to the ground and swiftly crushed it beneath his sandal, grinding it into a dark mass of legs and fluid.

Damien dragged her from beneath the palm and seized her so close to him that he hurt her against his hardness. She was shivering and clutching him and crying out: 'Take it away! Take it away!'

'It's gone, honey. It's gone.' He held her and tried to soothe her, but she couldn't forget the feel of those hairy legs clinging to her skin, and her fingers dug into Damien and she gave little moans as she moved her face back and forth against his chest. It had been a tarantula, she knew that ... fearsome things, like imps of the devil.

'It's dead, Wilda. It can't frighten you any more.'

But her attack of nerves had her in such a grip that she couldn't stop shivering, and with a sudden groan he tilted back her head and brought his mouth down on hers, and his lips tasted of the salt in the air ... after the horror she had felt there was a divine paradise to this, and she clung to him as if giving him her life, lifting her hands to cradle his black head, not caring any more if he threw her to the sand and slaked the passions suddenly let loose between them.

The surf washed in over the sands and the rocks, and time was lost out of mind as Damien had his will of her mouth ... there was no sanity any more, no world beyond this one in his arms. His mouth took hers with a sensual deliberation, taking care not to crush the feeling from her lips but teaching them, second by second, to respond and vibrate to the warm caressing movement of his lips until the feeling became so intense that she could feel her entire body pressing to him in an abandonment of sheer sensation, cascading through her until she moaned not with fright but with longing. He lifted her then and she felt the warm plush of the sand under her limbs, and she was helpless to resist him as his wide shoulders blotted out the sun.

All of her wanted his kisses; that delicious vibrant ecstasy not only on her mouth but her throat, her shoulders, her soft and silken hollows where the nerves were clamouring for his touch. She was tremblingly alive to her utmost, sensitive core and had never known such an excitement of her senses. His mouth upon hers was an urgent, provoking pressure now, arousing her to her very heart. His eyes through his dark lashes were glowing, sensuous, beckoning ... there was not a whimper of protest in her as he arched her over the muscle of his arm and she felt his mouth travelling down her body.

And then, just as she was melting into the lovely

mindless dream, he shattered it and dragged her down to earth, leaving her abandoned on the sand as he leapt away from her and turned his back on her, standing there taking deep raw breaths of air into his lungs, a hard quiver running all through his body, from his muscular legs upwards.

Still she lay there, dazed, and aware of a coldness seeping in where she had been so glowingly warm and alive deep inside her. Then she slowly sat up and adjusted the straps of her swimsuit with shaking fingers.

'Everything with us is extreme.' He turned and was in control of himself once more, though his eyes were still sultry as they dwelt on her. 'My mother's a sick woman and I behave like that with you, and in a manner of speaking you are in my charge. But you were so shaken up that I either slapped you out of it, or kissed you. Dammit, Wilda, why do you have to be so—so damned destructive to my resolves?'

He strode off along the beach away from her, until he vanished beyond the fringe of rocks that guarded a pathway out on to the road. Wilda had an idea he was going to climb into his car and drive very fast along the highway, and she didn't want him to do that in his present mood. If they had kissed, if they had again come close to losing all control, then she was as much to blame as he was. She had let the tarantula scare the wits out of her and even if a slap would have been effective in sobering her, there was no denying that she had responded to his kisses until they had given birth to needs beyond kissing.

She ran along in his footprints and he was just about to start his car when she emerged on the roadside. 'Damien, no!' She hastened to the side of the powerful vehicle. 'Come to the house, *kyrie*, and have that drink. You need it after the worrying news about your mother, and in this reckless mood—please, don't go driving, not like this. What if something happened to you? Would that do Madame any good if she had to be told that you—you——'

Wilda broke off and looked at him eloquently. He sat there, his hands gripping the wheel, and then he allowed his shoulders to slump and he nodded in agreement with her. 'I'll put the car away in the garage,' he said. 'You go on up to the house, and would you mind changing into something shapeless and drab and preferably nun-like?'

'My uniform?' Her eyes dwelt on his face as her nerves quickened, but she faintly smiled and tried to look unaffected.

'Yes—no. You must have a dress that might just take my mind off ravishment.'

With that he drove off in the direction of the garage, and Wilda returned to the beach to collect her tangerine rug and the canvas bag in which she kept her sunglasses and sun-lotion, not to mention a book she hadn't even opened.

She stood a moment watching the crests as they came dancing across the sea. The hot golden glow of sunlight had cooled considerably and a few low clouds had crept into the sky. It looked as if Damien's prediction of a squall was going to come true, but as she turned to make her way towards the house Wilda cast a regretful glance at that place where the sands were still disturbed from the turbulence of Damien's embrace.

It was easy enough to tell herself that she was no more than another woman to be conquered and enjoyed by him, but there had been a sweet delirium to those moments she couldn't dismiss; an electric, heart-swelling pervasion of feeling beyond mere gratification of the moment. She remembered the hot silky smoothness of his throat inside his shirt and the pulsating throb under the skin, where her lips had touched him. The great vein running from his heart and there under her mouth, the very life force of him. She had wanted him and felt no shame in the recollection of that need ... regret lay in the fact that she was just a passing phase in his life; a girl he desired for several obvious reasons. Her fairness of skin and hair in contrast to his darkness. The fact that she lived under the same roof and there was a certain titillation to it ... and most basic of all, at the very root of the fascination he felt and yet rejected, lay the memory of a girl clad only in a man's purple pyjama jacket, exciting him even as she seemed the most shocking little *amoreuse* he had ever come across.

Folded rug over her arm and a small frown wrinkling her brow, Wilda made her way into the house and went upstairs to her room. There she stripped off the sandy swimsuit and sought about in her wardrobe for a dress that he demanded be plain and simple and not likely to affect his senses as the blue and white swimsuit had done.

She decided that a skirt and pin-striped blouse should satisfy his illusion that what smouldered between them had anything to do with what she wore. In fact if the Biblical idea of the fallen woman was taken to its logical conclusion she should be clad in sackcloth and ashes. With a rueful smile Wilda brushed sand grains from her hair and arranged it in a smooth knot at her nape.

A glance in the mirror assured her that she looked neat and unobtrusive, and when she joined Damien in the *zala* she did manage to seem a lot more composed than she felt. She sat down in a deep chair, making sure her skirt was sedately arranged over her legs, no longer bare but clad in honey-toned nylon, with neatly heeled shoes on her slender feet. She watched Damien a moment as he shook a blender in which he had, from the labels on the bottles, mixed vodka Martinis. He had briefly looked her way, but was now concentrating on the drinks, and Wilda permitted herself the luxury of running her eyes up and down his tall, supple body in the tapered trousers and stylish shirt. The hunger opened and closed its lips inside her, like some undersea plant, and her fingers gripped the arms of her chair and she forced herself to look away from him in case what she felt was showing nakedly in her eyes.

She had always admired this room, whose semi-circular shape had a grace intensified by satinwood and kingwood finishes, lamps hung on slender chains, the muted gleam of long silk window drapes, and a lovely sculpture of a Greek goddess holding her draperies to her exquisite form and companioned by a Chiparus javelin thrower in bronze. All of this was presided over by a ceiling of delicate colour and tracery that produced the exact outlines of a web.

She felt Damien crossing the carpet towards her and with a casualness that was totally assumed she glanced up at him and gave him a cool smile as she accepted the drink he held out to her. She prayed, as she gripped the glass in her fingers, that her hand wouldn't tremble. She hoped it didn't show that the sparks were still there inside her, shimmering in her veins. He stood looking down at her as he took a deep mouthful of his Martini, looking into her eyes which had tiny violet shadows beneath them.

His black hair was still unruly, she noticed, still mussed from her hands, and then to her relief he went and sat on the couch, stretching his long legs across the carpet that was ivory-coloured with dark Greek patterns woven into it.

'The drink okay?' he asked.

'Fine,' she said, taking several sips and grateful for the warmth it imbued in her. 'What time did you think of going to the hospital, Mr Demonides?'

He glanced at his watch. 'Before dinner, I think. We can go and dine after we've seen *manoula mou*. I hope to God she's feeling brighter—what do you think could have caused that sudden relapse?'

'Could it have anything to do with your brother's failure to come and see her?' Wilda asked. 'She's very fond of him, isn't she? And when a person is sick it's so easy to get depressed over anything like that.'

'Yes, damn him, it could be his fault.' Damien looked moody as he applied his lighter to a cigarillo. 'Sorry to be smoking, after what you said, but I can't seem to give up on my—vices.'

'Whether you smoke or not is entirely your own decision,' she said quietly. 'I'm prejudiced.'

'Naturally so.' He ejected smoke from taut nostrils. 'Your father must have been in his prime when he died?'

She nodded and cradled her Martini glass, looking into her drink so as to avoid a meeting with Damien's eyes. She might weep if she showed her even a fraction of tenderness . . . there had been moments, plucked out of ecstasy, when he had touched her hair and her skin with fingers molten with a kind of tenderness, but it had been masculine wonderment at the softness and the silkiness, not the specific worship of a man in love.

It would be crazy of her to warm herself with the impossible hope that she had touched his heart.

There in the cool depths of her drink, where the chips of ice moved to the slightest tremor in her hand, she saw again the image of a woman totally submitted to the caresses of a man, whose skin was like that of the bronze javelin-thrower.

Oh, God ... she quickly lifted her glass and drained away the images until the ice was in her mouth.

'Wilda?'

She glanced across the room and found herself lost in Damien's eyes.

'Oh, God, Wilda!'

'Your mother's going to be fine.' Swiftly she set aside her glass and went to him, unmindful of the physical danger, caring only to comfort him. She leaned down and touched his shoulder, and right away his body tensed.

'The operation was a complete success, Dr Martinson assured you of that. Your mother's brooding, *kyrie*, wanting both her sons to be there to give their love and support. It's perfectly natural.'

'I guess you're right,' he sighed. 'It isn't until you come up against illness that your realise your own inadequacy. The person you care about is in the hands of other people and all you can do is hope and feel a sharp arrow of pain waiting in your guts—sorry if my language is graphic.'

'I understand how you feel, *kyrie*. I've been through it—I know!'

'But there was no chance at all for your parent, was there?'

'Absolutely none,' she said, feeling the old wound aching again in her heart. 'The doctors were quite frank with me. They usually are, Damien, and if they feared for your mother's life, they'd tell you so and not leave you to hope in vain.'

'I guess I'm hopeless where illness is concerned,' he returned.

'Most men are,' she smiled. 'You are awfully efficient at dealing with tarantulas.'

'Obscene things, and some of them bite.' He glanced up at her and a glint of the devil came into his eyes. 'You screamed blue murder, didn't you? Chilled the blood in my veins.'

'Which soon warmed up again——' She broke off, colour storming her cheeks. 'I mean, it's too easy to lose control.'

'Incredibly easy—with someone honey-soft and sweetly smiling as you, my pseudo-angel.'

'If you say so, *kyrie*.' Her smile faded.

'How submissive of you to let me!'

'A woman finds it exhausting to fight all the time.'

'Is that why you gave in—so deliciously?'

'Perhaps.' Her colour deepened and intensified the blue of her eyes. 'I'm a female ... I felt the biological urge and it would be foolish of me to deny it. I—I'm not made of marble.'

'You certainly aren't.' His eyes travelled over her pin-striped blouse, high at the throat and with long sleeves ending in tight cuffs. His lip quirked. 'Cool as a cloister once again, starched and prim, and on the outside so very proper. What are you at heart, Wilda? Blue-eyed angel or belladonna?'

'I'm my father's daughter,' she said softly. 'If you find that impossible to believe, then what more can I say?'

Damien studied her for what seemed a long time, then moodily he lounged against the cushions of the couch. 'Please pour me another.' He held out his glass to her.

'You'll be driving, *kyrie*,' she said cautiously.

'I could drive to hell and back on more than a couple of vodka Martinis, and furthermore, Wilda Bird, if my nerves are shot, then accept some of the blame.'

She took his glass and went to the side-table on which stood the blender. She poured him a refill and handed it to him. '*Efharisto poli*,' he said, half-mockingly. 'And do stop looking like a sister of mercy in the presence of a lost soul. Smoking is bad for me, and I mustn't drive if I've been drinking—heaven knows what fires I shall burn in for nearly seducing you under the palm trees. That *coup de grâce* would be something—were I first off the mark!'

'Do stop it, Damien!' Colour drained from her face and the tiny shadows under her eyes had the shape of violet petals.

'Stop smoking, drinking and wenching! You begin to sound like an echo of my father.' He laughed abruptly. 'From the rear, just now, you had the pure outlines of a choirboy in that outfit, but when you turned to me again you were every sweet, soft inch a woman. I could eat and drink you, Wilda Bird, and I believe I'm damn well going to.'

'Damien, what else have you had beside Martinis?' she asked.

'Brandy, my darling. A nice double brandy while you were upstairs putting on your nun's outfit.'

'You're intoxicated!'

'Just about, little one.'

'Then I shall drive you to the hospital, do you hear me?'

'Every word, honeybird, in that clear as an English

church bell voice of yours. You'll drive me to see Mamoushka.'

'And you'll do a bit of sobering up under the shower before we go.'

'Anything you say, wildbird. Anything you desire— I'm ready, willing and able, as the hosepipe said to the fire.' He smiled slowly, his eyes crinkling into velvety-grey wickedness as he lounged with his black head against an ivory silk cushion. 'Lovely Wilda Bird, have you any notion, I wonder, what a man feels when he holds you close to him, so warm and alive, so good at playing the sweet innocent?'

She walked away from him and stood looking out of a window at the darkening day. Across the sea the sky was grey shot with scarlet and she could hear the wind rattling the pensile leaves of the palm trees. 'I do believe there's going to be a storm,' she said.

'I do believe you may be right,' he drawled. 'Are you scared? Especially as you are going to do the driving—I hope you have an international licence to drive, and that you can handle a car like mine?'

'Of course I have the correct licence,' she replied. 'I have now and again taken Madame for a drive, when she's been in the mood. And I do have some experience of fast engines.'

'And where did you acquire that?' he asked, lazily.

'In Monte Carlo—' The words came out quite naturally, before she recalled who had taught her the difference between a supercharged engine and the one which had been under the bonnet of her father's old banger.

'Ah, sin city, where you learned the lot, eh?' Then, with a shocking suddenness, he sat up and quite deliberately hurled his empty glass into the curved fireplace, where it shattered against the slabs of sea-coloured stone. Just as suddenly he was on his feet and a couple of strides brought him the length of the room, where he paused and plucked Wilda against him and held her struggling body while he hurtfully kissed her mouth. He did it with a kind of impassioned ferocity, as if he were as angry with himself as with her. When he looked down at her fiendish little lights gleamed in his eyes. Wilda's were dilated and her nerves were vibrating ... this time there was no delirious harmony in their close embrace ... this was a snarling, bruising, frightening battle, and his reckless strength warned her that he could easily win it. A tormented moan broke from her and her fingernails broke against the hard muscles of his back.

'Your mother,' she gasped. 'You have to go and see her, Damien!'

'So I do.' He flung her away from him, so she stumbled and had to clutch at a table. It tilted and the object on it fell to the floor, its fall broken by the thick carpet. Breathing quickly, Damien bent to pick it up, the Greek goddess in half-concealing draperies. He gazed at it, his lips twisting.

'This reminds me of you,' he told Wilda, 'except that she isn't flawed.' He replaced the goddess on the table. 'I'm going to take that shower—I guess I need it more than I realised.'

When he was gone the *zala* still seemed full of him, and pressing a hand to her bruised mouth Wilda leaned her head against the window-pane and the tears slid down her face in unison with the rain on the glass. She had known that to love him would be the greatest emotional risk of her life ... she had fought so hard against it but had lost the battle, and right now felt unutterably defeated.

Oh, God, what was she going to do when one half of her wanted to run away, and the other half wanted to stay? And to stay with Damien was to be half in heaven, and half in hell.

The room darkened around her and the rain increased outside ... she must make her choice, but first she must go with him to see Charmides.


CHAPTER SEVEN

DAMIEN was stone cold sober when they drove into town, so there was no need for Wilda to insist that she take the steering wheel, aside from which the rain was falling hard and the wind was high, buffeting the car as they drove along.

Wilda sat there beside him, conscious every moment of what had transpired between them in the *zala*, bruises from his angry grip imposed on her arms, and a bruise from his kiss still stinging her lower lip. She wore her Somali leopard coat from the happy days with her father, when a musical composition of his had brought in a substantial cheque and he had insisted that she have a coat that would always look good. She was snuggled down in the fur, the collar high about her face as if she wished to hide herself from Damien. She still felt very strung up and on the defensive, but knew she would have to relax before she went in to see his mother.

Below the coast road the sea was being flung high

by the driving wind, and there was a hypnotic quality to the movement of the windshield wipers against the wide front window of the car. But silence hung between Damien and herself, and they had entered the town and were approaching the tall lighted shape of the hopsital before he spoke. 'If you're waiting for an apology, then you'll wait all night,' he said, in a curt voice. 'Nothing tries my temper so much as that wide-eyed air of innocence you assume with regard to your activities in Monte Carlo. Why can't you at least be honest and admit you were there for a good time, and that if it went sour you had no one to blame but yourself?'

'As I've told you before, Mr Demonides,' she said, making her voice as hard as his, 'my activities in Monte Carlo, as you call them, have nothing to do with you.'

'While you work for my mother they have everything to do with me,' he rejoined. 'You've been at Moonside almost a year and she has grown to trust and depend on you. I wouldn't want her let down in any way—and don't tell me to mind my own business again, because I have a specific reason for hoping you're trustworthy —and reformed.'

'Thanks,' she said, 'but there's no need to concern yourself to that extent, for when you leave you won't be leaving your mother in the charge of someone who may revert to her *demi-mondaine* ways and invite all the local he-men to your mother's private beach. As I have already told you, I'm leaving Moonside just as soon as Madame is well enough to accept my notice. I'm going back to England.'

'I see.' He was silent a moment. 'I hope I'm not driving you away?'

'You're driving me to see your mother, aren't you? Can't we leave it at that?'

'I imagine we must, for the time being.' He turned the car into the parking area of the hospital and directly he switched off the engine Wilda released herself from the car and stepped out on to the ground. The wind rushed at her and blew tendrils of her hair about her neck and the rain drove against her skin. She ran towards the entrance and entered the reception lounge ahead of Damien. It was a very modern building, with an express lift that swept them to the floor on which Charmides' private room was situated.

Just about halfway along the corridor there was also a small waiting-room for the relatives and visitors, and Damien suggested Wilda wait there while he went along to his mother's room to ensure that she was awake and prepared for visitors. He swung the door open, and then stood utterly still for a moment. Wilda, just behind him, could see a couple of other people in the room, a man and a woman, but she didn't realise that there was any real significance to Damien's startled manner until he spoke.

'Troy!' he exclaimed. 'Good lord, I had no idea you were here!'

'You wouldn't have,' his brother replied. 'Charlotte and I only arrived in Key Laguda about an hour ago and we came straight to the hospital. I concluded you would be coming to see mother, so I didn't bother to phone you.'

'I'm glad you're here—at last.' Damien widened the door and stood aside so that Wilda could enter. She felt suddenly an intruder and wished Damien's brother had telephoned the house; she could then have excused herself from this visit, which had suddenly become very much a family one. She looked curiously at Troy and it startled her that she saw very little of Damien in him. He definitely resembled his mother and at first glance was the better-looking of the two men, but what Damien lacked in symmetry of features he abundantly made up for in vigour and build. Also his hair was blacker ... everything about him was much more masculine and definite.

Troy stared back at Wilda, running his blue-grey eyes up and down her slim figure in the leopard coat. Her cheeks were slightly flushed from the wind and the rain, and her eyes were incredibly blue in contrast to her very fair hair. Wilda wasn't to know it, but her kiss-bruised mouth gave her a slightly sultry look, and Troy's eyes narrowed as they moved to his brother.

Damien was studying the woman called Charlotte, who was clad in a beautiful suede coat and a Russian cossack hat, a pair of expensive pearl studs clipped to her earlobes. On her engagement finger, as she raised a hand to smooth a thin dark eyebrow, she wore a blazing heart-shaped diamond. Her mascaraed eyes were fixed upon Damien, and she looked every inch a young woman of background, poise, and the kind of education only the best European schools provided. The type who would look sensational in ski clothes, or Italian beachwear; confident and certain of her place in Troy Demonides' life.

'I must introduce you to my fiancée,' Troy said, and he put out a possessive hand and closed it upon the suede sleeve of Charlotte's arm. 'I daresay Mother told you I was going to be married, Damien? Well, this is my girl, Charlotte Highsmith, whose family have a famous law firm in New York.'

'I'm glad to know you, Miss Highsmith.' Damien

inclined his head but didn't hold out a hand to the girl; instead he reached for Wilda and drew her into the family group. 'And this is Miss Grayson, Mother's companion. She was good enough to come with me to pay Mamoushka a visit. If you have seen the doctor, Troy, then you'll have been informed that Mother has not been too well today. I believe she's been fretting over you—have you been in to see her?'

Troy nodded, and Wilda noticed how his mouth had thinned. 'She did get rather upset and the nurse suggested that we wait here awhile until she was feeling a little more composed. The doctor tells me that the operation went very well——'

'Yes,' Damien cut in, 'but that doesn't alter the fact that Mamoushka is no longer a young woman, with the vitality to overcome surgery as swiftly as you or I. Earlier today when I called in she was very listless and that's why I brought Miss Grayson along to help cheer her up.'

'It was good of Miss Grayson to come,' Troy said, rather coldly. 'But Mother now has an abundance of visitors, so it would seem that her companion has had an unnecessary journey. I want Mother to meet Charlotte and to get to know her——'

'I daresay you do,' Damien interrupted. 'But all the same Wilda is going to say hullo to Mother—let's face it, old man, I wired your office days ago and then nothing more was heard of you. You could have left word where you'd be in case you were needed, but I was informed that you couldn't be located.'

'No——' Troy looked faintly uncomfortable. 'Charlotte and I were invited by this Greek millionaire to stay on his yacht, and then we took off on a short cruise, and you know how it is——'

'Sure,' Damien drawled. 'But it's a change for you to put pleasure before business. If your Charlotte is having a humanising effect on you, then I'm glad to welcome her into the family.'

Charlotte gave a soft laugh when he said that, and immediately he looked at her and the soignée brunette held his eyes with her dark ones. It was a look Wilda couldn't help but notice, and she decided that it was inevitable ... a woman would have to be vegetable, mineral, or neutered not to notice that Damien had the excess of *zoikos* in the Demonides family.

'Come along!' Hard fingers abruptly gripped hers and she was led to the door. 'Miss Grayson usually has a soothing effect on Mamoushka, and as you've waited this long, Troy, you might as well wait a little longer.'

Wilda was marched along the corridor and ushered into Charmides' room, where a young nurse had just finished applying face-powder to the rather pink-lidded eyes of the patient, propped up against very white pillows and looking rather weak and woebegone.

'Wilda—dear!' She held out her arms. 'I've missed seeing your pretty face!'

'I've missed seeing you, Madame.' Wilda smiled and went to her, and then overcoming a slight shyness she bent and kissed Charmides' cheek.

'Now you're not to get all tearful and silly again,' said the nurse, casting a reproving look at her patient. 'Your children are anxious for you to get well so you can go home with them, so no more crying and throwing vases of flowers over the floor. I have to do the clearing up, remember, and my poor feet are aching enough without having to run back and forth with floor mops. You're going to be a good girl, promise me?'

Charmides gave a sudden chuckle, and lightly stroked Wilda's soft cheek. 'I've a very bad temper, nurse, and I'm truly sorry. I always aim things when I get annoyed.'

'Well, you save up all that energy and get well on it.' The nurse returned Charmides' repentant smile, and then made for the door. She glanced at Damien, who was hovering and looking very dark and overpowering in the clinically white room, which though furnished with a vanity-table and a small wardrobe, was still obviously a hospital room.

'I'd like to speak with you, nurse,' he said, and the next moment he had followed her from the room and closed the door, leaving Wilda alone with his mother.

'Sit down, child.' Charmides indicated an armchair near the bed, and Wilda obeyed her, reflecting at the same time that Charmides had passed on to Damien a tendency to aim things when he was annoyed—though it seemed a mild word to describe the ferocity with which he had aimed that Martini glass and plucked her into his arms. The colour heightened in Wilda's cheeks and Charmides stared at her.

'You're a beautiful child, aren't you?' She leaned to one side and picked herself a grape from a huge bunch, dark purple and bloomy. 'Has that big dark boy of mine noticed? Yes, I bet he has! I hope he's behaved himself while I've been laid out in this damn bed, subjected to needles and pills and other indignities?'

'Mr Demonides has been concerned that you get well and come home, madame, as soon as possible. Moonside isn't the same without you.'

'Mmm, you probably mean it, don't you? I've noticed, Wilda, that you only say what you mean, and keep quiet rather than be insincere. Has Damien seen Troy?'

Wilda nodded. 'He's in the waiting room with Miss Highsmith, his fiancée.'

'And what is she like?' Charmides studied her rings. 'She kept him away from me, do you know that, while I was damned ill in this place. At any other time he'd have dashed home to be at my side—I suppose he's head over ears in love with this young woman?'

'I rather imagine so, Madame.' Wilda gave Troy a fleeting thought and wondered if he was capable of being madly in love with anyone; he had struck her as rather superficial, and she realised, with a sense of surprise, that she was again comparing him unfavourably with Damien. Of the two brothers there was no denying that Damien had the deeper nature, and that meant a whole lot more feeling. Passionate feeling, she realised ... yes, that was what Troy appeared to lack. Handsome, well-dressed, smooth from top to bottom, with none of the rocks and crevices that made Damien a harder proposition for a woman, and at the same time a far more exciting one.

'Is she good-looking?' Charmides asked, turning her rings round and round on her fingers. 'Is she dark or fair?'

'Brunette, madame, and very attractive—and self-assured.'

'Yes, she would be, but Troy probably needs that in a woman. Do you know why I've always shown my love for Troy more than I've shown it for Damien?'

'Because Damien is the stronger of the two,' Wilda replied. 'Not only in a physical sense, but in a psychological one. He can go his own way without needing a guiding hand.'

Charmides nodded. 'He's harder, his feelings are deeper down and have to be dug for—like gold, I suppose. Strangely enough he'll make the better husband of the two because he'll never put his business before his pleasures with his wife. I only wish——' Charmides drew a deep sigh, while Wilda felt as if her stomach contractions were going to make her cry out. How desperately she felt like giving vent to that cry ... Damien, wildly in love and putting before everyone and everything the woman he took for his wife.

'He's definitely got himself mixed up with someone,' Charmides said worriedly. 'I've tried to make him talk about her, but he treats the whole thing almost mockingly—it won't do, Wilda, if he's going to marry because he feels he must. He'll make her life hell if he does that, for he'll feel cheated and if there is one thing that boy can't abide, it's to be cheated. He'd give the shirt off his shoulders, but if you cheat him—his father was the same. It's being Greek, you see. They're a proud lot, but God help a woman if she fails to get at the heart of such a man. I—I think I failed where Helios was concerned, or perhaps it was being a self-made man of business that took all his emotions and left me high and dry on a kind of pedestal. He wanted a beautiful wife—much as Troy wants the same—as an adornment for his home and to create envy among his business associates. It works if the woman is prepared for such a life, but I—I was rather romantic, Wilda— a little like you, I feel.'

Again she reached out and touched Wilda's cheek, moving her hand down to the collar of the leopard coat. 'Suits you, my dear. The kind of coat a man buys for a woman, or am I being too curious?'

'My father bought it for me, madame. I have a sort

of love-hate feeling for it as the skins are real and I hate the thought of lovely creatures like leopards being slaughtered to adorn women—life is such a mixture of cruelties and complexes, a—and one clings so to the kindnesses.'

'Quite so, Wilda. You're sensitive, and life is always that much harder for those with a sensitive soul. That man who hurt you, have you got over him yet?'

'Him—oh yes, madame!'

'I'm pleased, Wilda. But that means you might go and fall in love in the future, and I don't want to lose you—yet.'

'Madame——'

'I think I should see Troy again, and that fiancée of his. Be a dear child and tell them I'm perfectly composed and won't make another scene. Troy does hate scenes, which is not the case with Damien. He quite enjoys a battle royal and even as a baby he used to love it when a squall struck Key Laguda and threw the waves high into the air. Helios would hold him in his arms on the veranda at Moonside and he'd chuckle with delight as the wind howled over the water and it splashed in right to our roof. It's a pity—ah, but there's no going back, and we can only look ahead and hope for the best. Go and tell Troy I want to see him and make the acquaintance of his young woman.'

'Yes, madame.' Wilda rose to her feet, and vivid in her mind was a picture of Helios Demonides with his firstborn son, holding him aloft to watch the storm, delighting in the fact that his baby boy was so fearless. Her heart seemed to swell with the love that was as painful as it was pleasurable.

She leaned down and kissed the powdered cheek of

his mother. 'Get well soon, madame,' she said fervently.

'I plan to, child. I was moping over Troy not being here, though I will say Damien has been an unusually good boy since I took sick. Has he been kind to you?'

'Of course——'

'There's no "of course" about it, my girl. Damien's the sort of man who isn't always kind to a woman he might admire. Something else would get in the way before kindness—his need to be her master, I fancy.'

'I—I wouldn't know, madame.' Wilda flushed, hating herself for a liar, but she could hardly admit to Charmides that she carried on her mouth the mark of Damien's imperious behaviour with a woman.

'I wonder.' Charmides watched the colour on Wilda's cheekbones. 'A man would have to be weak-sighted or emasculated not to notice a girl like you, and I know my son Damien well enough to know that he has eyes like a hawk and the sensual instincts of a jaguar—he's noticed you, and he's made a pass, hasn't he?'

'Well——' Wilda felt and looked slightly hunted.

'Yes, he's tried something—did you like it?'

'Madame!'

'Don't be coy with me, Wilda. Has he kissed you?'

'Y—yes.'

'Did you enjoy being kissed by Damien?'

'I—I suppose I did.'

'Suppose! Of course you enjoyed it! He's a man, and women have been reaching out for him with greedy hands since he was a boy. That's what used to infuriate Helios, and you might as well know that Damien got sent down from his prep school on account of the young wife of one of the masters. Shocked?'

'Not terribly.'

'I wonder why?'

'He's atractive to women.'

'Is he attractive to you, Wilda?'

'I—I suppose so.'

'Do you think you could take his mind off this other girl who has her hooks in him? I don't want him marrying someone he may not love.'

'Madame,' this time Wilda was shocked, 'I'm not employed at Moonside as a distraction for your son!'

'All the same I think you could distract him, and I'd sooner he fell for you——'

'I—I'm going now, madame. Goodbye!' Wilda hastened to the door. 'I'll tell Troy right away that you want to see him.'

Wilda escaped from the inquisition, a well-meant one, but far more tormenting than Charmides could have guessed. When she arrived at the door of the waiting-room, which was slightly ajar, she stood a moment collecting her scattered composure ... and then from inside the waiting-room she heard Troy say something that instinctively drew her hand back from the door handle.

'I knew Mother had a companion at Moonside, but I imagined she was a sensible, competent type of woman. Let me be perfectly frank, Damien, this girl might have all the qualifications of a companion for *you*, but Mother needs someone a little nearer to her own age and a little less decorative. Someone properly qualified as a nurse, perhaps.'

'Mamoushka is not an invalid,' Damien retorted, 'and she won't be one when she fully recovers and leaves hospital. I think I know what's really troubling you, Troy. Mother's told you of her intention to have a codicil added to her will stating that Moonside is to become the property of Wilda Grayson. Am I correct?'

'Too right you are!' Troy snapped the words. 'The idea is absurd—the result of a fevered mind. We can't allow that little chit to get away with such a thing!'

'How petulant you sound, Troy.' There was a derisive note in Damien's voice. 'You have all that gilt the *patir* spent his life accumulating, and yet you begrudge a roof over the head of a young woman who doesn't have a home. You're getting greedy, brother.'

'Family possessions should stay in the family,' Troy said, with such a sharp edge to his voice that Wilda flinched and backed away from the door she had been about to push open. 'I shall certainly oppose this foolish idea of Mother's—be realistic, Damien, that house is built on its own private beach and worth a great deal of money on today's property market. We can't permit a sick women to get quixotic notions in her head just because this young woman has used her undoubted charm to get round her. That's what Wilda Grayson has been up to, but I suppose you can't see further than her big blue eyes. She's been getting round Mother and insinuating herself to such an extent——'

Wilda didn't stay to hear any more. She hastened towards the lift and all she wanted was to get away from the hospital as fast as she could. She fled along the white-tiled corridor feeling hurt and rather stunned. Troy had spoken as if she were a schemer who had wheedled her way into his mother's good graces, but the very idea of receiving Moonside as a bequest struck her as crazy. Wilda certainly didn't take it seriously, but she did feel driven to get away from Troy's insulting remarks.

The doors of the express lift slid open and she stepped quickly inside and pressed for the ground floor. As the lift swooped downwards she huddled into her

146

leopard coat and decided bleakly that she couldn't return to Moonside, not with Troy there harbouring such uncharitable ideas about her.

She thought of the huge diamond on Charlotte Highsmith's left hand, and the note of derision in Damien's voice when he had asked his brother if he hadn't yet got all the money he desired. The Charlottes of this world were the ones who arrogantly assumed that life was Pandora's box and they were entitled to rifle it of all its contents, letting loose the discontent on which many a marriage had been wrecked.

Out of the rain Wilda sped ... running from the barest mention of being given a house because she had shown a lonely woman a little kindness and consideration. As luck would have it a cab was being paid off at the hospital entrance and she was able to scramble inside before the rain soaked her.

'The Club Dinarzade, please.' She had spoken the words to the driver almost without thinking, and then as she sank back against the leather of her seat she realised that she had obeyed a subconscious desire to see Kenny Devine and be comforted by him ... the only man in Key Laguda who truly understood the kind of person she was. She gave a little sigh, and for the first time that day felt safe from the demands of the Demonides family.

Only by getting away once and for all from that family would she be able to make another life for herself, for there was no future in what she felt for Damien. He played havoc with her heart, and while she stayed within his disturbing orbit she ran the constant risk of giving way to feelings that could lead her into real trouble ... the kind that any self-respecting girl shrank from.

When he kissed her she was no longer in control of her own emotions ... he released inside her a primitive response to him that was exciting beyond anything she had ever known. It was like finding the other half of herself, as if she were incomplete until Damien drew her against that vibrant body of his and she felt herself come fully, gloriously alive. He made her yearn to submit to the passion he aroused in her, and from that she could only awake to find herself one more girl who had let foolish heart ruin her life. She wasn't experienced, and complete surrender to Damien could lead to a complication she could well do without.

A little shiver ran through her, not of coldness but of something electric, tingling ... ignited by what Charmides had said about Damien as an infant, held in his father's arms to watch with wonderment the high squally waves lashing at the sands of Moonside beach. Her heart seemed to turn in her side and she could feel her fingernails, several of them already broken, stabbing into the palms of her clenched hands. All that she felt for Damien had to be faced ... she was consumed by love of him, and could hardly endure the thought of that other girl Charmides was against him marrying ... a girl in trouble which Damien had to put right.

Wilda stared unseeingly from the rain-swept window beside her. The cab was stalled in a traffic jam and she was grateful for these moments of respite, of being alone like this so she was able to build a small reservoir of composure before confronting Kenny. She knew exactly what she was going to ask of him ... to get from Damien her passport and papers so she could fly away as soon as possible from Key Laguda. Perhaps if Damien were out of sight he might in a while be out of her mind, and Charmides would be all right now that she had both her sons in attendance.

The traffic eased a little and the cab started forward again and in a few more minutes was pulling to a stop in front of the Club Dinarzade. Wilda paid off the driver and fought the gusts of wind and rain as she went in under the canopy of the club entrance. She entered the deeply carpeted foyer and feeling somewhat bedraggled made her way to the powder room in order to tidy herself before taking the interior lift to where the band would be playing.

No one tonight would be going up in the scenic elevator which she had travelled in with Damien, when a silver lunar moon had softly lit the sky and the air had been fragrant with flowers. Now everything was being unmercifully lashed by the storm, and there would be no dancing on the roof terrace tonight.

Upon leaving the powder room, her hair softly combed and left loose about her shoulders, and with colour applied to her lips because she had looked rather pale, Wilda approached a waiter and asked if Mr Devine's band was playing in the restaurant. He inclined his head and skimmed his eyes over her face and her leopard coat. 'Is madame awaiting her escort?' he inquired.

'I'm a friend of Mr Devine's,' she replied, saying it with assurance because it was true. 'I wondered if there might be a table available—I haven't booked but——'

'You are in luck, madame.' The waiter smiled. 'On such a night as this we have received cancellations and if Madame would like to come this way I can offer a table quite near to the orchestra.'

'Thank you.' Wilda followed him into the softly lit dining-room and at once she heard the romantic, rhythmic beat of Kenny's music playing a dateless dance tune from an old Astaire-Rogers movie. Only about half the tables were occupied and as promised she was placed at a table, normally for two, at an angle to the orchestra platform where at the moment Kenny had his tuxedoed figure turned away from her so he didn't see her hand her coat to the waiter and sit down. The waiter brought her a menu and because her last meal had been a light lunch she ordered peeled shrimps on a slice of melon, and a butterfly steak with mashed potatoes and French beans.

A wine waiter hovered and on impulse Wilda asked him to select half a bottle of a not too heavy red wine for her. Kenny would join her when he realised she was here and could get away from the band for a few minutes, and the wine would help both of them to relax. She needed to look relaxed so that her request wouldn't appear too desperate. Still it was essential to her to keep her desperate private feelings to herself. She would let it be assumed—and it was half the truth —that Troy Demonides thought her too young for the role of companion to his mother and she wanted to leave without further argument.

She sat there, her fingers playing idly with the sprig of fern attached to a single pink rose in a flute of glass. The band moved smoothly into another melody and Kenny slowly turned in order to play his gaze over his audience and assess their mood ... when his eyes found Wilda his baton again provided an erratic beat that his boys were too experienced to follow. The music proceeded smoothly as Kenny came down the few steps from the platform and made his way towards her. Like an actress taking a cue Wilda curved her lips into a smile. 'Hullo,' she said. 'Aren't you flattered that I came through the storm in order to enjoy your music?'

'*Mein gold!*' When deeply moved Kenny always reverted to the language of his colourful Stepney upbringing. 'To see you here on such a night is indeed a pleasure! Look, the place is half empty!'

Wilda held out a hand to him and he clasped it warmly. 'Can you join me for a little while?' she asked. 'I've ordered wine and I hoped we might have a drink together.'

'I shall be delighted.' He gazed down at her and slowly searched her face. 'You bring a little trouble with you, Wilda, I see it in your eyes.'

'I'd hardly call it trouble,' she said, and hoped her lightness of voice didn't sound too forced. 'But I'm going to ask you to do me a favour, as an old friend.'

'Not too old and not too much of a friend, I hope,' he said, looking quizzical. 'But excuse me for just a minute, Wilda, and then I'll join you in a glass of wine —my boys, as you can hear, manage quite well without their *Taktschlaeger*—their time-beater.'

'I'm sure that it's the result of very efficient rehearsals,' she smiled.

While Kenny was absent from the dining-room the waiter arrived with her first course, and also the wine was opened and almost unaware she took her cue from Damien that evening they had dined here and waived the pretentiousness of tasting a wine from the cellar of an exclusive club. He filled the two glasses, as she indicated, and gave her a keen, knowing look from dense Italian eyes. She smiled a little and the waiter inclined his head as if he believed he was dealing with a woman of the world. Wilda could have informed him that she had learned one or two very vivid lessons from a man of the world ... oh, God, she mustn't think

151

about Damien except as someone she would never see again. She would remain in town tonight and stay at an hotel.

She was eating her shrimps and melon with a piquant sauce when she saw Kenny making his way back to her. He laid something beside her plate and she drew her breath and picked up the orchid, a swirl of cream petals with splashes of deep violet. 'I was going to send it to you,' he said. 'The chef has been keeping it on ice for me.'

'Oh, Kenny, it's perfect! What a dear person you are!'

'For me, Wilda, you are like that orchid—lovely and rather a mystery, a lot wise and a little foolish ... kind, sweet and a little sad.'

'That's a song writer talking.' She gave a slightly confused laugh.

'Not entirely.' He took the chair that faced her own, and he watched as she drew her lips across the velvety petals of his flower. 'It's a man saying the things he should have said four years ago. Instead of sweeping you off your feet with ardour, I proposed we get married so I could take your father's place. No wonder you turned me down! I must have sounded such a prig.'

'I've always thought you kind, Kenny,' she smiled. 'A man I could trust and respect, but four years ago I was too young for marriage, and you were starting to make a name for yourself in the music business. It would have been unfair to let you take on the responsibility of a wife.'

'It would be a stick of a man who ever regarded you as a responsibility.' He lifted his wine glass to her. 'Shall we drink to a happy meeting and no more parting?'

Wilda lifted her own glass, tempted to let it go at that, but too honest to do so. 'I've decided to return to England, Kenny.'

She saw his fingers grip the stem of his glass, then he drank some of the wine. 'And why is that?' he asked carefully.

'A touch of homesickness, I think.' She sipped her own wine and found that it recharged her courage. 'But there is a problem and I'm going to ask you to help me resolve it.'

'I see.' He sat back in his chair and his slanting eyes took on a shrewd and very Israelite look behind the lenses of his spectacles, the kind that always made him look a little like pictures of Glenn Miller. 'Are you answering the call of nostalgia, or are you running away from a man?'

'A man!' The nerves twisted inside her. 'What makes you say that?'

'Perhaps because I am a man myself. Eat your shrimps, they look so good.'

She picked up her fork, but her appetite had lost its edge, and she was strangely unsure of this man who had lost that boyish uncertainty of four years ago. Then he had seemed at times very young for his age, and at other times almost a contemporary of her father; a playmate or a counsellor, but never a lover. Now she cast him an uncertain look and realised that like herself he had undergone new experiences in the years that had separated them; he had probably had love affairs, and success had given him an undoubted polish. Wilda bit her lip ... time didn't stand still and it was going to be more difficult than she had realised to ask of Kenny that he confront Damien for her.

'I regard you, Wilda, as ultimate truth on two slim

legs,' Kenny murmured, 'so out with it, or I shall start guessing the trouble.'

'I'd hardly call it trouble——'

'What you call it, and what your eyes reveal are two different things. It's the tall Greek, isn't it? You have become involved with him despite what you told me, that he means nothing to you.'

'He can't mean anything to me.' There was a desperation in her voice that wouldn't be held back. 'He has someone else in his life, and apart from that his brother is set against me as companion to their mother. He thinks I'm too young—oh, Kenny, I want to get away—I must—but Damien has my passport and I won't—I can't see him to beg for it!'

'So you are afraid of this—Damien?'

'No—not afraid, exactly.'

'I think I know what you mean.' Kenny was frowning thoughtfully. 'There was a force about the man, a look of privilege and power, as if always he has pleased himself.'

'Yes,' she nodded, 'that describes him.'

'The conquering type, eh?'

'From his size elevens to the crown of his head,' she said, with feeling.

'I don't have to be Freud to know why you don't want to face him any more, Wilda. I could see that he'd be attractive to women.'

'Like a panther, Kenny, but only a very foolish female puts out her hand to stroke that lovely beast.'

'Did you put out your hand and stroke Damien Demonides?'

The question struck at her like an arrow, winging its way to those nerve centres Damien had invaded ... yes, her hands had stroked that sleek warm skin, and her lips had touched him, feeling the vibrancy of him pulsing under her mouth. A thousand little slivers of hot steel seemed to fling themselves through her veins, and she felt like groaning with the pain and the loss of what had been so emotionally exciting ... a rapport of the body and the senses she would never feel again. She had wanted it too much, and might want it again, and so she had to get away as soon as possible, put an ocean between them.

'You don't have to answer me.' Kenny rose to his feet. 'Right now, Wilda, I have to get back to the band, but we must talk. Tonight, with the weather so bad, people will leave as soon as they've dined and the band will pack up earlier than usual. Stay right here and wait for me, eh?'

She nodded and gazed up at him appealingly. 'Y—you don't think too badly of me, do you, Kenny?'

'I blame you for nothing, Wilda. You could never think or feel with anything but your heart—but I hate **it that any man should make you suffer. Just another** hour, *mein gold*, and then we can get away. We'll go to my apartment.'

He walked away to the orchestra platform before she could make some kind of protest ... his apartment sounded too intimate, and she was no longer so certain that he was still the Kenny Devine she had known in the old days ... too shy to touch her.

# CHAPTER EIGHT

WHEN Kenny's band slid smoothly into *Bei Mir Bist Du Schön*, the haunting Sammy Cahn song, the restaurant was all but empty and Wilda sat alone in the shadows and finished the ice-cream and cherry syrup which Kenny had instructed a waiter to bring her ... in memory of summer days when they'd enjoyed the confection together. She listened to the music and knew that when this number ended the boys would pack up their instruments and it would be time to leave the club ... to depart for Kenny's apartment.

It seemed so puritanical to object, but she could never completely forget her experience at Monte Carlo ... there she had trusted a man and been cruelly disillusioned, and she couldn't quite dismiss the idea that Damien might come looking for her when she failed to return home to Moonside.

Lost in her anxious thoughts, she gave a start when a hand touched her shoulder. Giving a little gasp, she glanced up. 'It's only me,' Kenny reassured her. 'Did you enjoy your sweet?'

'Delicious,' she smiled.

'Good.' His eyes travelled over her face. 'Shall we be off?'

'I—I have to settle my bill.'

'That's all been taken care of.' He lifted her coat and held it in readiness. 'Come along, Wilda. We have to talk, don't we?'

She stood up and slipped her arms into her coat,

which he drew around her, holding her a moment with his fingers buried in the leopard fur. 'Kenny——'

'I'm listening, honey child.'

'I—I must see about booking into a hotel for the night.'

'That I realise, but you need to talk with me and we shall be more relaxed at my apartment. Luckily it isn't far from the club; I'm told the winds are blowing a gale and there has been damage to local cables carrying the electricity. Let's hope the streets aren't blacked out and we can make it in the car.'

As they passed the members of his band, who were busily packing up for the night and exchanging wise-cracks, Kenny paused to collect his coat, which made him look dashing with its dark fur collar.

'Have fun, Kenny,' one of his boys called out, giving Wilda a wink. 'That's quite a dish you have there, man. Can I come along and play mood music on my sax?'

'Get lost,' Kenny said jovially. 'But be sure you're at rehearsal tomorrow morning.'

'Will you be there?' was the dry retort.

'Say goodnight to them,' Kenny smiled at Wilda.

'Goodnight, boys,' she said obediently.

'GOODNIGHT!' chorused the entire band, while the sax player followed them from the dining-room with a cascade of sparkling notes.

'They're just a bunch of charming brats,' Kenny said affectionately. 'Don't mind them and their in-sinuations.'

'Oh, I don't mind,' she smiled, but somewhere inside her she was inclined to wonder if she told the truth. The Kenny of those ice-cream and cherry syrup days was submerged in a man of purpose, who was rather disturbing in his smart overcoat. He led her from the club into a street where the lights were out on one side of the road, and as they hurried to his car he had to hold her in the crook of his arm because the wind was so rough. The rain had lessened but the wind was making a kind of booming noise, and the lights that hadn't yet been affected were giving ominous blinks, some of them almost dimming out.

'We'd better get home fast,' said Kenny, handing her into his gleaming roadster the colour of rich cream.

'How affluent you are these days,' she said, sinking back into a veloured seat.

'Why not?' He joined her in the car and quickly closed the door against the force of the wind. His eyes crinkled as he turned to her for a moment. 'And just look at you—you really had my boys stunned, so grown-up and gorgeous with your sun-washed hair and skin. Made me feel ten feet tall, what they were thinking.'

'What were they thinking, Kenny?'

'That I'm taking you home to make love to you.'

'And are you going to do that?'

'Would you want me to, Wilda?'

'I want us to talk, Kenny. You promised to help me.'

'I'll help you get away from the Greek ... there was never any doubt in my mind about that. It's the doubt in your mind I'm worried about.' He started the car and they moved out on to the road, where in the comparative dimness the sudden oncoming headlights of other cars were like great blurred flowers that burst against the windshield and threw petals of light over Wilda's tense face. It seemed as if every way she turned she came up against this problem of physical attraction, which drove out reason and filled the body with urges and demands that caused actual pain unless they

158

were assuaged ... in the right pair of arms. Those arms for her were hard and brown, with the muscles moving like whips of silk under the warm skin, locking her to Damien, from whom she must break free because she could never belong to him in the way she wanted to belong.

An affair with him could never be enough ... if a man really wanted a woman, then he allowed nothing to stand in his way. He swept aside all the barriers and consigned to the devil all that was in the past and gave himself to the future.

In this day and age too many couples thought it smart to mock at marriage, but at the root of their mockery lay a stone that would always stop the relationship from flourishing. The fact that the man or the woman didn't feel a passionate commitment; the need for the sacrament and purification: the symbolism and ritual of a wedding service. The vows exchanged in solemn but beautiful surroundings, the scent of white lilies, the ring and the rice. There was a beauty to it, and Wilda felt a shaken, swooning need to experience it with Damien ... or to have nothing at all.

She came out of the reverie into which she had fallen when Kenny pulled into the forecourt of a block of apartments and cut the engine of his car. He sat for a moment, moving his hands on the wheel, and all around them was the bluster and whine of the gale force wind. Spots of rain came against the windshield, and Wilda gave a cold shiver.

'Make up your mind, Wilda,' Kenny murmured. 'I think I have the strength of mind to turn the car around and take you to that house on the beach, if that's what you truly want. But I'm warning you that once you come back into my life I'm not going to let you go again, so choose right now.'

Wilda had made her choice and there was no going back on it. 'I'll wait inside the entrance while you put your car away in the garage,' she said. 'You don't want it damaged in this fearful wind.'

'You mean that?' In the dashboard glow his face was serious, almost stern, without a hint of triumph, as if he sensed that she had torn her heart-strings in making her decision to cut free from Moonside and the man who at this very moment was probably watching the storm from the seaside veranda.

'It's a nice car,' she said, a trifle evasively. 'You don't want anything to happen to it.'

'No,' he agreed, 'as it's on credit—like much of our lives.'

Wilda slipped out of the car and the wind whipped at her hair and took her breath as she ran towards the glazed doors into the foyer of the apartment block. In the old days Kenny had not been cynical, and as she stood breathlessly in the foyer she wondered again if she had been wise to come here with him. She could have insisted on going to a hotel, but there in an impersonal room she would have been terribly alone with her commitment to a future without Damien.

All or nothing, and if he came here looking for her and found her with Kenny, whatever had been between them would be finished once and for all. That would be the *coup de grâce*. He would believe that she had come home with Kenny in order to spend the night with him ... for Damien her basic integrity had been flawed by that incident at the St Cyr and from the very start, even as they were mutually attracted, it had gnawed away at him.

If he discovered her with Kenny the frail threads of

his belief in her would be torn apart and there would be nothing left to hold them together.

Love, she reflected, had masochism in it; all mixed with the passion, the excitement, and the giving. Kenny came through the doors and took her arm. They went to the lift and he pressed for the tenth floor, and it was as they stepped into the corridor that every light went out in the building and they heard the mechanism of the lift grind to a halt, as it became stalled between the floors.

'Damn, that's torn it!' Kenny stood very still, and then began searching his pockets while Wilda felt the alarmed beating of her heart and realised that the storm-damaged cables had given out and plunged Key Laguda into darkness.

A darkness that was dispelled into mysterious shadows as Kenny spun the wheel of his cigarette lighter and played the flame over the numbers on the apartment doors until he reached his own and fitted his key into the lock. 'Careful as you go,' he said, as they stepped inside. 'I have one of those battery reading-lamps, which I always travel with as they're handy, so you wait just here, Wilda, while I fetch it.'

He moved away, taking the little flame with him, and Wilda stood in the darkness and realised that she was stranded here in this tenth floor apartment, the lift out of action, and that long flight of fire stairs leading only to a blacked-out street, where only a fool would drive a car. Reasonably speaking there was no way of getting away until the power was restored, and that could take hours in a gale that would be lashing at the broken cables, making it unbearably hazardous for the men working on them.

Kenny emerged from his bedroom and he was carrying the small lamp which gave a fair amount of illumination in the thick velvety gloom. 'Are you nervous?' he asked, and the light gleamed upwards over his face, revealing his slight smile and making his eyes faunish and mysterious behind the rimless lenses. 'A good thing the power failed after we got out of the lift. At least we can share the comfort of my lounge.'

Wilda followed him into the room, and he set the lamp down on the coffee table and gave a quiet, almost conspiratorial laugh. 'Maybe this was meant to be,' he said. 'Had we been on our way to Moonside, we'd now be in danger of driving off that coast road into the sea ... can you imagine what that sea is like, all maddened by the wind?'

And as he spoke Wilda curled her hand against her heart and had a sudden awful vision of Damien driving in this direction along that road, coming in search of her!

'I hope to God——' There she stifled the rest of her sentence, holding in her heart the fierce hope that Damien had been too annoyed by her flight from the hospital to bother himself about her. If he had surmised that she had turned to Kenny Devine, then that might be enough to keep him safely at home, scowling on the veranda of Moonside as he watched the gale-swept sea, confirmed in his belief that she was the kind of woman who needed a variety of men.

Kenny removed his prosperous overcoat with the dark astrakhan collar and tossed it across the back of a club sofa. Then he came to Wilda and drew her leopard coat from her slender figure ... she tautened, feeling him close to her in the muted glow of the lamp, aware of his eyes upon her hair, which the wind had blown into a turbulent wave above her eyes.

'I can't get over how grown up you are—you're an exciting woman for a *goyim*, do you know that? Of course, you were distractingly pretty as a teenager, but now—now you're ice *bombe*, bursting with chilled cream and the tang of bitter cherry. I very much fancy you, *mein gold*.'

'It's the moody lamplight and the sound of storm,' she said lightly, turning away from him and sorting about in her bag for a comb. 'I must look as if I've been blown through a hedge—how long do you reckon the power will be cut?'

'Who can guess?' He stood there stroking the fur of her coat, and Wilda tried not to notice and wondered if he was aware of giving away his thoughts in that gesture. 'I expect you realise, Wilda, that you'll have to stay here with me—in this blackout the roads will be extremely hazardous and I can't allow you to walk to a hotel, if you have that in mind.'

'I hope I'm not a fool,' she rejoined, tidying her hair in the little mirror of her vanity-case. 'I hope for the sake of friendship we both value that neither of us is going to allow the blackout to—to upset our sense of balance.'

He gave a quiet laugh. 'What a polite and very British way of putting it, Wilda!'

'You're British as well, aren't you, Kenny?'

'Yes and no,' he smiled. 'I'm now the *shtarker* of my own gang.'

'Big shot.'

'We've both changed since we've been apart,' he added. 'I'm not any more the shy and diffident East End boy your father befriended, Wilda. We've both grown up and have to face each other as a man and woman.'

'Kenny,' she faced him squarely, 'I came to you as a

163

friend, because I need help, but I'm not unaware that a sense of danger accelerates the emotions. That's all it is really. A man and a woman alone in a high-up apartment, cut off from the world below by a belt of darkness, seeing each other by the light of a lamp and feeling that primal urge to reach out and cling. But it couldn't mean anything lasting or real—I'm going home to England. It's where I want to be!'

'To brood about someone who has hurt you?' he asked.

'I'm not hurt,' she denied. 'I'm facing up to reality.'

'You told me the Greek meant nothing to you, but when a woman runs away from a man there has to be more than a negative reason behind it. Has he made love to you?'

'In the X-certificate sense, do you mean?' she said, rather sharply. 'I—I didn't come here to face an inquisition, Kenny, and we're both adult enough to know that because two people feel a physical attraction it doesn't necessarily have to mean that it's a lifelong passion and devotion.'

'So you were physically attracted to the Greek?'

'Yes.' She flung back her hair in a defiant gesture. 'Yes, if you must know. I'm not made of marble—haven't there been women in your life, Kenny, whom you've wanted, as Damien wanted me, for just a passing pleasure?'

'So that was it?' he murmured. 'An affair with no future to it?'

'We never had an affair.' Suddenly she felt weary and sank down into one of the club armchairs, leaning her head back against the leather, her hands gripping the arms. 'That's what I want to avoid—an empty affair that leaves a bitter taste of regret—but he has my passport, as I told you, and other documents relevant to my getting a job. I must have them, but I just can't face him to ask for them. You have to understand and bear with me, Kenny. I'm being what they call a woman.'

'Of course,' at once his tone of voice was gentler, 'and I am being what they call a brute. What you need is strong sweet coffee, but with the power off we can't use the percolater. We shall have to make do with a drink instead—I have some French cognac. Will that do?'

'Lovely,' she said, and really felt the need of something to revitalise her and at the same time relax her. It wasn't being alone with Kenny that made her feel like this, even though she realised that all the latent foreign charm had come awake in him, making him far more smoothly sensual than was entirely safe. She touched his orchid, which she had fixed to the waist of her plain skirt . . . in the old days, long before Damien, would she have loved Kenny had he been the way he was now, aware of her as a woman, and with the shyness unlocked from his tongue so he was able to say schmaltzy things and be a little brutal? A woman wanted both, in long heady draughts, there was no denying that . . . the caveman roughing up, and then the intoxicating making up.

She watched him in the shadows, pouring cognac at the side table, and knew how easy it would be to turn completely to him, a friend and lover who might stop her from hurting so much inside, where the tearing apart from Damien had caused a wound that wouldn't heal very easily or swiftly.

Outside in the night, the dark impenetrable night, the world seemed at the mercy of the howling wind, rattling the apartment windows and pounding the very walls for entrance. 'Please, God, please,' she silently prayed, 'let Damien be at home and not out there on the windswept road in the awful dark. Oh, God, I couldn't bear it if anything happened to him because of me!'

She couldn't forget ... she had to go on remembering every detail of being with him. Even tonight at the Dinarzade she had relived every second of her evening there with Damien ... dancing in his arms ... gambling with him in the subdued lighting of the gaming room, feeling the stress and tension of faces and bodies, the glamour of winning, the bated silences as the cards were turned on the green surface of the tables, and the roulette wheel dropped its ball.

She had known, heaven help her, that once burned in Damien's Greek fire she would never come fully alive for any other man. Charm she would be aware of, a warmth she might want, but never again would there flood over her that total yearning to give everything of herself, heart, body and soul, into the immolation of ecstatic flames that slowly burned every inch of her ... his mouth, his touch, his passionate whispers in a Greek that never came out of the textbooks.

She quivered and tried to make her eyes like still water as she saw Kenny approaching her chair, holding out a brandy glass in which was a generous shot of cognac. 'This should settle your nerves,' he said, placing the bulbous glass in her hand. He sat down in a chair facing hers and raised his glass. 'Salud!'

'Kali hara,' she rejoined, almost without thinking.

He stared at her a moment, then took a mouthful of his brandy, while she did the same. Then she held the glass cupped in her hands and it was large enough to have held her fast-beating heart. 'I can't help it,' she thought. 'That's how it will always be, for Damien the Greek is there inside me.'

'Will you do it?' she asked. 'Will you go and see him and ask for the return of my passport and papers? His mother keeps them in her private desk, to which he has the key while Madame Demonides is in hospital. I—I'd be terribly grateful, Kenny.'

'Grateful enough to sign on with me as my resident singer?'

It was her turn to stare at him. 'You aren't serious?'

'Never more so, Wilda. Now don't look at me as if I'm suggesting the impossible—there was always a little flame throbbing in your voice and even when you were eighteen it could express subtle nuances. I've never forgotten the way you sang *Stille Nacht* for your father, a little while before he died. It was haunting, and I remember the way he smiled, as if there would be no more pain, and I don't believe there was after that. The doctor said not, do you remember?'

'Every moment, Kenny. Every detail.' Wilda's eyes in that moment were all tears and shadows, and suddenly she was too inwardly stricken for more than a *moue* of distress, which she stilled with a deep swallow of cognac. It burned warm inside her and eased that terrible lump he had brought into her throat. Still night, silent white corridor a week later, along which she had run seeking Kenny and the shield of his arms, where the grievous tears racked her. Oh, why couldn't she feel for Kenny all that she felt for Damien ... it would be so easy then to say she would sing again and travel with him and the boys, finding new places to see, and learning how to laugh again.

'You have singing style of a rare sort, Wilda,' he said, a little note of urgency coming into his voice. 'There's a place for you, and I'd love you with us, quite frankly.'

'I—I don't know that I want to be a *chanteuse* again, Kenny. It didn't really work for me before, that kind of life. You know, the excitement of singing to people, and then the lonely room afterwards, and the thoughts.'

'Yes, but this time you'd be with me and the boys, and such a thing as loneliness wouldn't come into it.' He leaned forward, earnestly. 'As if that would happen with us, little *knodel*—mouth like a brandied cherry and sweet—God, how sweet! When we leave here, we're travelling to Bergenwald to start a sixteen-week season at the Linden Schloss, a rather classy Alpine hotel catering for folk who like to ski during the day and dance at night in the fantastic shadow of the glaciers and gorges. Doesn't your imagination take fire? Austria at violet time, when the snow melts on the lower slopes and the carpets of *veilchen* are un-veiled. Coloured mountain *huttes*, walks in the woods, and damson wine in a *weintrube garten*.'

He paused and his eyes crinkled. 'Then at night a big carved bed with a goose-feather puff to keep you snug.'

She heard him distantly, for when he spoke of the *veilchen* he sent a quiver of remembrance right through her ... Damien's name for her eyes!

'It all sounds very nice,' she said carefully. 'It should be an exciting booking for you and the band.'

'I'm inviting you along, Wilda. I look at you and imagine how it could be for us, among the baroque castles and old courtyards ... a new life, *mein gold*. The start of something precious. Come, aren't you tempted?'

'Of course,' she admitted. 'I have a fair share of Eve in my veins.'

'That sounds as if you think of me as a tempter rather than a man who wants to help you forget the devil who has hurt you? No, I don't mean physically, but in your emotions. Be reasonable, what have you in England to go back to? Your father was a travelling man, so you have no home there, and as I understand it no relatives to whom you are really close. Won't you be lonely there, in a London bedsitter, doing some unglamorous job when you could look charming cradling a guitar and singing in that evocative voice which I bet has grown in warmth and womanly appeal, as you have.'

'You flatter me,' she murmured. 'I'm terribly out of practice, both as to the singing and the guitar playing.'

'Those can soon be remedied and you know it. Wilda, with me and the boys to back you, you can be a sensation—with your looks, your style.' He kissed his fingertips. 'I know the business very thoroughly now and I think I could make a star of you.'

'Kenny, you sound like——' She broke off, biting her lip. Oh yes, he tempted her with his offer, and he underlined in stark words what her life in London would be like. She wasn't a trained nurse, so if she took work in a hospital it would be very menial ... of course, she could become a maid-companion again, but she couldn't visualise finding another employer like Charmides. Though troublesome at times, demanding of time and attention, she had been a woman of character and a certain charm.

'Why do you hesitate?' Kenny regarded her with perplexed eyes. 'I offer you bright lights, the excitement of trains and planes, that satisfying burst of applause at the end of a number.'

'I must have time to think about it, Kenny.'

'You shall have it,' he said eagerly. 'We finish at the Dinarzade in eight days—the world was created in seven.'

She smiled at him. 'How persuasive you've become!'

'It's the Yiddish in me.' His eyes were faunishly amused. 'What do you truly want, if it isn't to be a star?'

'I don't know——'

'I think you know in your heart even if your mind won't agree. Tell me!'

'I can't——' She moved restively and glanced towards the windows, behind which the wind was unmercifully whipping around the building, as if it would tear the glass from the frames and the bricks from the mortar ... a dangerous sound that tightened the nerves to breaking point. 'Will that go on all night, do you think?'

'I imagine so, but we're safe enough here,' he reassured her. 'I wouldn't care to be out in it ... it's grown powerful enough to blow a car off the road. Wilda, you're trembling!' He moved as if to come to her, and she shook her head at him, eloquently. He shrugged and sat back again, and after a taut moment of silence set about applying the flame of his lighter to a Half Corona. He smiled quizzically at her through the smoke.

'You're a romantic,' he said, 'and I believe you are looking for the kind of love that's a heaven and a hell—oh yes, that's the kind the romantics go for. They want to touch the stars and taste the bitter wine, crazy as it sounds.'

'It is crazy,' she agreed, but knew in her heart that it was true. There had been moments when she had swung towards the stars in Damien's arms, and there had been other times when they had quarrelled fiercely and the bitterness of his words had been almost impossible to forgive ... that last time in his arms he had called her a flawed goddess, his eyes ravishing her even as he rejected her.

'My father,' Kenny went on, lounging there with his cigar and his cognac, 'was a wise and industrious tailor who spent most of his life sewing suits that often outlasted the men who bought them, and he said that in a true marriage the couple fitted each other like a pair of sleeves in a well-cut coat. They had to be a matching pair, as if on fate's assembly line they were made for one another. He worked so hard, that Yiddish poppa of mine, and he died when I was fifteen, soon after my sister Sharon married. It was at her wedding I heard my poppa say that about love and marriage and I never forgot it, for it sounded so right, somehow, that somewhere there might be a girl made for a guy, and that through all adversity they would come together and fit each other like those sleeves, and suit each other down to the smallest stitch.'

'You speak like a romantic yourself, Kenny,' she smiled.

'Doomed to suffer before getting the love of my life?' He spoke lightly enough, but he was watching her with an intensity that made her very aware of their aloneness high above the darkened street, shut in with the wind howling around their eyrie. She briefly wondered what she would be feeling if she were stranded like this with Damien ... would it be excitement, the thrill of response as their eyes met across the shadowy room?

Wilda rose to her feet, making a sharp movement

with her hand as if to ward off her own tormented desires ... desires that mustn't find their release with Kenny, whom she liked but didn't love, whose life she couldn't upset just as he found success and deserved to find real content with a woman who wouldn't always be looking over his shoulder for the figure and face of another man.

'It's just occurred to me,' she said, 'that if the battery runs out in your Aladdin's lamp, then we'll be in total darkness.'

'Too true.' He glanced at the lamp. 'I hope it doesn't give out.'

'It could happen, Kenny. We should think about making ourselves comfortable for the night.'

Wilda meant the words quite unprovocatively, but Kenny chose to accept them as an invitation. 'We'll be snug as a pair of bugs in there.' He gestured at the door that led into his bedroom. 'There's no sense in a pair of adults not facing up to the facts ... I want you and you need to be with someone who won't frighten you but cherish you.' He moved towards her as if to take her into his arms. 'Once committed, all the rest will fall into line, the Austrian tour, singing with the band, maybe even making things permanent——'

'No, Kenny!'

'What?' He came to a halt as if struck across the face. 'But you said——'

'That we should make ourselves comfortable.' Wilda spoke firmly, and looked around her. 'If you have a quilt, then I can bed down on this sofa and be quite all right until the morning.'

'You're kidding me, Wilda!' A glint of anger had come into Kenny's eyes. 'You don't provoke a man and then calmly inform him that you really intend to sleep on a sofa. I won't let you!'

'Then I'll leave and take a chance on the dark streets.' Wilda turned to pick up her coat and handbag, quite prepared to walk out into the stormy night rather than face any more male temperament. She had trusted Kenny to behave only as a friend, but it was more than ever obvious that he wanted to be her lover ... there was no denying his attractiveness, his warmth of heart, and it would be easy enough to find comfort in his arms, but when the morning came she would be faced with a hard task, that of telling him that no other man was ever going to replace Damien in her heart. She would be but an automaton responding to kisses that meant absolutely nothing, and there would come a time, inevitably, when she would hurt him without meaning to ... when she would whisper a name that would not be his.

Be adult, Kenny had said. This was the best way she knew of being adult, by walking out rather than play-ing a game of makebelieve.

She was at the door and about to open it when Kenny spoke in a defeated voice. 'I'd forgotten that underneath that sun-gold hair and sweet face you had a will of sterling silver. You haven't changed, honey child, but I guess I've let my conquests as leader of the band go to my head. You must stay here—I promise to be good.'

Her fingers clenched the doorhandle and then re-laxed. She turned to him and the resolve was still there in her face ... she would have walked out, obeying an impulse of despair which had taken root in her from the moment she had fled from the hospital, away from the sound of Damien arguing with his brother about her. She realised too late that she should have gone straight to a hotel, stayed there until the morning, then telephoned Troy Demonides to ask for her passport and papers. He would have been only too willing to let her have them.

'I'm just not ready,' she told Kenny, 'to get involved with anyone in an emotional way. I don't mean to hurt your feelings, but a one-sided love can be hell. I should know! I've been through it!'

'That Greek must be hard as nails,' Kenny exclaimed. 'Putting you through hell when you were made for heaven—God, what a crass fool I was four years ago! I could have made you mine with a bit more force and not so much callow fear that you'd come apart if I grabbed you and kissed the breath out of you, so you couldn't say no to me. Ye gods, I had to behave like some knight of the holy grail, and you flew away from me like some golden moth I'd actually caught, straight into the clutches of that damn Greek, with his fierce white teeth, his black hair, and heart of iron.'

Kenny took a deep breath and shook his head in total perplexity. 'What does he want—a heiress? Does his sort only marry for money? Doesn't a man like that care that a lovely golden girl is worth more than a gold brick?'

'It isn't money,' she said, with a sigh. 'He has a committment to someone else, and apart from that——' She broke off, for it seemed as if Kenny didn't know about the St Cyr scandal and this wasn't the time to enlighten him. 'There was just too much in the way, Kenny. His family would never approve of me.'

'Quite frankly, Wilda, he hardly looked the sort who would care two decimal pennies what his family thought of his private life—a very high and mighty devil he seemed to me.'

'That's the way it goes,' she sighed. 'We don't ask, do we, to get our hearts broken against a rock. I tried not to care for him. I told myself he was only after some fun during his vacation at home, but it seems that we aren't in complete control of our hearts and mine opened up to him without my consent, if that doesn't sound too Freudian. I have to get away from him, Kenny. I have to get away on my own so I can try and forget him.'

'Won't that defeat your purpose?' Kenny frowned as he regarded her. 'When we're on our own we tend to fall back on thoughts and memories, to live with them rather than seek company to dispel them. I think you'd be wiser to come to Austria with me and the boys— unless you're afraid I might get out of hand?'

'I—I don't know what I should do for the best—not right now.' Suddenly she felt very weary and wanted only one thing tonight, to lay her head on a pillow and sink aeons deep into a dreamless sleep, undisturbed by despair until she faced it again in daylight, refreshed by slumber and perhaps no longer in doubt about what she should do.

'May I borrow a quilt and a pillow?' she asked. 'I'm so terribly tired I want to fall asleep and forget the sound of that wind out there.'

'You'll have the bed,' he said firmly, 'and I don't want an argument about it.'

'But I'll be perfectly all right on the sofa——'

'Hush your sweet mouth, honey, as Rhett said to Scarlett.' He grinned and picked up the battery lamp. 'Great film, wasn't it? Remember when we saw it at the

Regal, all that long time ago? Yes, romantics, the pair of us.'

He led her into the bedroom and placed the lamp on the bedside table. 'You can have this, until it runs out. I have my lighter and can make do with that. Will you be okay, Wilda? You won't be scared by the wind at the windows—just listen to it! Like some wild animal trying to get in!'

'I'll be fine,' she assured him. 'You're a very kind man, Kenny, and that's why I don't want to hurt you. You do understand?'

'I do, regretfully.' His smile was quizzical. 'Needless to say I'd rather be hurt by you than any other girl I know. It would be quite an experience—okay, okay, I can see those big blue eyes frosting over and I'll make a real nice exit.'

He walked to the door, where he paused a moment more and murmured a couple of lines from *Bei Mir Bist Du Schön.* '"*Bei mir bist du gut ... Bei mir hast du It ...*"'

'Translation?' she murmured, with a smile.

'You are a girl who is good, and you have It. Satisfied?'

'What girl wouldn't be? Goodnight, Kenny!'

He bowed, smiled, and withdrew, closing the door halfway, and then calling through the gap. 'There's no need to lock this.'

'Then I shan't. Kenny—you're forgetting the quilt and a pillow.' She took them from the bed and carried them to him, his eyes holding hers as he accepted them. 'Sleep tight,' she said, and firmly closed the door between them.

Alone in Kenny's bedroom Wilda unpinned his orchid and stroked a finger across the velvety petals ...

why couldn't it be he who raced her pulses and set fire to her emotions? Why did it have to be a man who only wanted her for a while, only to discard her when his conquering instincts were satisfied? She gazed across at the rattling windows and her thoughts sped to Moonside, where the peace she had found there was as transformed into turbulence as Key Laguda itself, rocked and pummelled by a fierce gale that wouldn't abate, with a failure of all power to add to the nerve-racking experience.

Again she hoped that Damien had not set out to find her when she had failed to return home to Moonside.

Removing her blouse and skirt, Wilda slid into the bed and clicked off the little lamp in order to preserve the battery. The darkness was complete, like a great cloak of black velvet wrapped around her. She closed her eyes and sought escape from the sound of the storm, and from the thoughts that milled restlessly through her mind. The things Charmides had said ... Troy's accusation that she had schemed her way into his mother's favour ... Damien's derisive mockery of his brother's greed.

Wilda pressed her face into the pillow and ached to forget her last bruising encounter alone with Damien, still feeling an intermittent throb in her lip where he had fiercely kissed her and then flung her from him, accusing her of being flawed.

The tears gathered and she blinked them fiercely away. She wouldn't cry over Damien ... she would do her utmost to forget she had ever known him, or the excitement he could arouse in her just by looking at her. Oh, God, why did he have to be so damnably attractive to her, from the first moment they had confronted each other on the starlit beach of Moonside, the water running down over his lean torso, losing itself in his black hair.

Wilda quivered at the memory ... was that really all she felt for Damien, a physical desire that could have been quenched and left her free to seek real happiness with a man like Kenny? If she and Damien had gone all the way in their lovemaking, would she now feel free to go with Kenny to Bergenwald, to sing again and feel the charisma of a tall Greek fading from her mind?

Why did she hesitate to go with Kenny to Austria? Was it because she didn't want to commit herself to another man in case Damien really cared for her?

Oh, she had to sleep or go quietly crazy in the dark. She pleaded for sleep to take her, and in a while it did, and she might have slept on till the morning except that in the depth of the night, with the gale still raging outside, she awoke to find herself sitting bolt upright, clutched by an acute sensation that something was terribly wrong. Had she heard a scream ... or had it been the screech of a car braking?

She craned forward in the dark, straining to hear beyond the wailing of the wind and the sudden buffets against the walls of the building. A clock ticked on the bedside table, and her heart seemed to pound inside her like a drum.

Suddenly the darkness was torment and she switched on the lamp. The clock revealed that it was half-past three in the morning and in a while she decided that a dream had awoken her, and with a reluctant hand that shook a little she turned out the lamp again and settled down with a worried sigh. She hadn't felt so tense, so aware of a feeling of doom, since the early days of her father's illness. During that time she used to wake suddenly in the night, as if someone in pain was calling for her.

Sleep had fled and she lay there until the pale light of dawn began to filter through the curtains, when at last the wind began to drop to only slight skirmishes that brought rain pattering against the windows. The sound of the rain had a soothing effect and Wilda drifted off into a dreamless slumber from which she didn't stir even when Kenny came in quietly to fetch a clean shirt from the chest of drawers. She was totally unaware that he stood a long moment beside her bed, watching her as she lay asleep, her pale gold hair spread across the pillow and a slim arm flung outside the covers, her fingers clenched in the top sheet.

Kenny was gone from the apartment when Wilda awoke to full daylight, clouded over by the drizzling rain. He had left a note for her in the lounge, along with warm, sesame-seeded rolls from a local bakery. The note read: 'Dear Sleeping Beauty, the rolls were baked in a fire-oven at a Yiddish bakery and you'll find them delicious; there is butter in the fridge, and eggs, and I've left the coffee on the stove. I'm driving to Moonside to collect your papers and your belongings, and I've made up my mind that you must come to Bergenwald. I can't dream of you being alone in the world ever again. Your Greek has the glamour, but I think I have the heart. Think about it! Yours ever, Kenny.'

Wilda smiled pensively, then went into the bathroom to freshen up, after which she made breakfast and found the rolls as delicious as Kenny had promised.

She turned on the little radio in the kitchen and thought what a relief it was to have the power restored after that long night of noisy darkness, and as she drank her coffee she listened to the local news, interspersed by commercials.

'Once again, good people, we are here happily to inform you that all power is back to normal and the heavy squalls have receded. There were various accidents in the blackout that followed last nights downfall of the local electrical cables, one of which caused several fatalities and injuries to motorists in a pile-up on the coastal road into Key Laguda's main thoroughfare.' The radio voice paused dramatically, and Wilda found herself tensed for the next announcement. 'The pile-up happened just before midnight. when about five cars were in an accordion collision with a bus travelling from the opposite direction. Two of the motorists were so badly burned as to be unidentifiable as yet, and the rescue operations were much hampered by the very dark conditions of the road. Those severely injured were taken to St Benedict's Hospital here in Key Laguda, and we have a report that three of those people are in a critical condition ...'

The news trailed off into yet another commercial, and Wilda sat with her coffee cup clenched in her hands and remembered how she had awoken in the night, as if to the cry of someone in agony.

Then, sensing that she was no longer alone, she slowly turned her head and found Kenny standing in the kitchen doorway. He lowered her suitcase to the floor, and withdrew a long beige envelope from his pocket and brought it to her.

'His brother was there,' Kenny said, almost casually. 'He made no difficulties about letting you have your things. The maid packed them for you, while he fetched the passport and papers from his mother's desk ... I was just on the point of leaving when this tall young woman came down the stairs. Very attractive, long brownish hair about her shoulders ... she came across to me and caught me by the arm. "Hasn't Troy told you?" she asked. "I think Miss Grayson may want to know that Damien was hurt in a car accident last night and they have him in the hospital ... he kept asking for her, but we didn't know how to get in touch with her. He was coming to look for her when the accident occurred." '

Kenny paused and gave Wilda a bleak look. 'I wasn't going to tell you,' he said. 'All the way back I kept telling myself there wasn't anything in it for you, that you'd be better off without him, that I could care for you and make you happy when you finally left off thinking about him. But it was what that girl said ... that he kept asking for you. If you'll put your coat on, Wilda, I'll drive you to the hospital.'

They didn't speak much on the way to St Benedict's. 'I knew,' Wilda kept thinking. 'I knew something was wrong.' Her throat thickened and she didn't dare to face the possibility that she was going to find another empty bed when she reached the hospital, stripped of the patient who had lain there and called her name.

'He'll be all right,' Kenny murmured, sensing the agony of mind she was in. 'That high-nosed brother of his would have been at the hospital had they placed Damien on the danger list.'

'I don't really know about that,' she said huskily. 'They don't get on ... it's funny that Damien should be classed as the hard member of the family. Troy is made of stone.'

'So you think——?'

'All Troy cares about is the family possessions.' Wilda

dismissed him with those words, and was out of Kenny's car as soon as they halted at the hospital entrance. He came in with her and there at the reception desk she was in such a state of anxiety that it was Kenny who had to make the inquiries.

Yes, Mr Demonides had been brought in around three o'clock in the morning, being among those who had carried out rescue work following the horrific crash on the coastal road. No one had been aware that he had been injured himself until he collapsed. They were given the number of his room, and Wilda found herself clutching Kenny's hand as they got into the lift and it swept them upwards.

'I mustn't cry,' she kept telling herself. 'He'll throw something at me if I burst into tears.'

They arrived at the door of his room, from which a young nurse was just emerging. She was flushed and smiling to herself, but when she saw Wilda the smile vanished. 'Is it all right for us to go in?' Kenny asked.

Wilda shot him a wondering look. The nurse nodded and Kenny swept open the door and they entered the clinically white room in which Damien looked aggressively dark, sitting up in bed, no pyjama jacket on, and pale strapping all the way around his chest. He stared at Wilda, his eyes like flamy steel in his face that was still rather ashen about the chin and lips.

Kenny, suddenly masterful, propelled Wilda towards the bed. Her legs felt as if they were stuffed with wadding and when she reached the bedside she swayed a little and had to clutch at the locker beside the bed.

'Look,' said Kenny, almost with aggression, 'before you say anything damned insulting to this girl, I'm going to tell you about her. She's the sweetest, kindest, most sincere and generous creature you'll ever have the good fortune to meet again. Why she cares for someone like you is way beyond me, but she does, and if you dare to hurt her one more time, Mr Demonides, I'll get a horsewhip and come after you with it. I knew her when her father was alive and they were just about the two best people in my life after my own father died. Yeah, sure, she was at my place last night, and if you make anything of that I'll bust a few more ribs for you!'

Damien gazed at Kenny in sheer amazement. 'D'you think I'd let you, Mr Devine?' he drawled.

'Boys—' said Wilda, suddenly furious in her utter relief that Damien was so wonderfully alive, his amazing vitality having thrown off the worst effects of bad bruising and cracked ribs. His delirious pain last night would have been caused by the stabbing pains in his chest and the exhaustion of helping to pull other people out of their smashed vehicles, until finally he had keeled over himself and been brought to the hospital around the time she had woken up in the pitch dark, reacting to him even though they were several miles apart.

'Boys,' she cleared her throat, 'if you're going to have a slanging match, then I'm going home.'

'To his place?' Damien demanded, scowling at Kenny.

'No—to England!' she said fiercely. 'I've had about all I can take from you, Damien. Life around you is just one everlasting battle——'

'A love battle?' he asked, and his voice was gratingly soft and he was holding out a rather torn hand to her, amber with iodine. 'I nearly went out of my head last night, wondering where you'd got to—then I remembered Devine was in town and I was coming to yank you out of his arms, had you been in them.'

'She wasn't, more's the pity,' said Kenny, hunching into his overcoat with the astrakhan collar. 'Well, you two, I'll be off to the club. The boys and I have some new numbers to rehearse and the time is getting on.'

'Kenny,' Wilda held his eyes for a long moment, 'good luck in Bergenwald. You'll have a great time there.'

'It could have been the greatest.' A shadow of sadness came into his faunish eyes, and then he shrugged and glanced at Damien. 'This girl's the marrying sort. I hope you know it, Apollo.'

'Kenny,' Wilda gave him an appealing look, 'I told you—there's someone else. I'm only here to make sure Damien's all right——'

'She's delirious,' Damien told Kenny. 'There's no one but her—there never has been. I've known I was going to marry her from the moment I saw her at Moonside.'

'Damien—you told your mother—you told me——'

'I told both of you there was a girl I had to marry, but first I had to find out if I could endure not being her first lover. I discovered that I could endure anything except one thing—losing you, Wilda. I rampaged all over this hospital looking for you after you left my mother's room. I drove back to Moonside like a fiend, searched the beach, even wondered if you'd gone swimming and got yourself drowned. Then I thought of the Club Dinarzade and decided to look for you there ... the rest you know. There was this almighty collision on that blacked out road, and cries and chaos for the next few hours. Then one of my ribs caved right in and I went out like a light.'

Their hands clung, and their eyes, and neither of

them heard the door close quietly and finally behind Kenny Devine.

'I love you,' Damien murmured. 'I love you madly. I quite simply, Wilda Bird, can't live without you.'

'You believe bad things about me,' she said shakenly. 'Can you live with that?'

'It was sheer raging jealousy,' his fingers gripped hers and began to pull her to his bed. 'My heart should have told me sooner that you were just a scapegoat in the Sadlier divorce, entirely innocent and blameless ... and unblemished when his wife dragged you from that hotel room. But I'd been seeing you each night, singing in the restaurant, and you looked so—so darned pure. I was planning to speak to you, and then that scandal exploded ... why in hell didn't you cry out to me in that corridor that night? I was there, watching what happened, and it was like a nightmare. I went out and sat in an all-night bar and by the time I left I was drunk and yet stone cold sober. I went back to the St Cyr, packed my bags, checked out, and tried to forget you. Then in one of Troy's letters there was this mention of a companion called Wilda ... in the end curiosity brought me home to Moonside. The moment I saw you on the beach that night I knew I had fallen for you, hook, line and sinker.'

'Yet you wouldn't believe me ... that I was quite innocent and had never had an affair with Myles Sadlier.'

'I'd never been in love before.' He drew her closer, until he could pull her down on his bed. 'Going to forgive me?'

'For being so pigheaded and Greek?' She smiled and lifted a hand to his face, tracing the line that clefted his hard jaw. 'Possessive and proud, aren't you?'

'Do you think you can cope with such a monster?'
He drew her hand to his lips and began to kiss her
fingers.

'Oh, I don't know that I'd call you one of those.'
Little thrills were running through her, and the love
fire was smoking and smouldering in his grey eyes. 'A
bit of a demon, perhaps.'

'Lovely Wilda Bird, love makes men unreasonable,
and I love you to my Greek bones—and you're woman
enough to have felt it!'

'Oh yes.'

'Then——?' He reached for her, and the next instant
gave an agonised cry. 'Damn and blast these ribs!'

'Damien darling, do be careful.' She was all solici-
tude, and as the pain ebbed a light of pleasure stole
into his eyes, slowly igniting them.

'For a while you'll have to do the lovemaking,' he
said. 'I'd love a kiss, *agape mou.*'

And like some brown-skinned, sensuous pasha he lay
back against his pillows and enjoyed the luxury of her
soft mouth caressing him. 'By the way,' he murmured
against her mouth, 'I had something with me when
that crash happened last night. It's in my jacket pocket,
if you like to look.'

'In a minute.' She kissed his throat and felt the pulses
throbbing under her lips, and she smiled, utterly certain now that his wild, proud heart beat for her.

In a little box in the pocket of his jacket there was a
pearl and sapphire ring, inscribed inside the gold band
with a word in Greek script.

'What does it say, darling?' she asked.

'Forever,' he murmured.

'Forever,' she echoed softly.

# What readers say about Harlequin romance fiction...

"Harlequin romances give me a whole new outlook on life."
S.P.,* Mecosta, Michigan

"Thank you so much for all those lovely hours of entertainment."
K.Z., Whiting, New Jersey

"Harlequin is the best in romantic reading."
K.G., Philadelphia, Pennsylvania

"Thank you very much for letting me subscribe to Harlequin romances."
M.J.B., Hendersonville, North Carolina

"A pleasant way to relax after a busy day."
P.W., Rector, Arkansas

*Names available on request.

# Take these 4 best-selling novels FREE

**ANNE HAMPSON**
gates of steel

**ANNE MATHER**
sweet revenge

**VIOLET WINSPEAR**
devil in a silver room

**JANET DAILEY**
no quarter asked

# *Harlequin Presents...*

## Take these
## 4 best-selling novels
## FREE

That's right! FOUR first-rate Harlequin romance novels by four world renowned authors, FREE, as your introduction to the Harlequin Presents Subscription Plan. Be swept along by these FOUR exciting, poignant and sophisticated novels . . . . Travel to the Mediterranean island of Cyprus in *Anne Hampson*'s "Gates of Steel" . . . to Portugal for *Anne Mather*'s "Sweet Revenge" . . . to France and *Violet Winspear*'s "Devil in a Silver Room" . . . and the sprawling state of Texas for *Janet Dailey*'s "No Quarter Asked."

Join the millions of avid Harlequin readers all over the world who delight in the magic of a really exciting novel. SIX great NEW titles published EACH MONTH! Each month you will get to know exciting, interesting, true-to-life people . . . . You'll be swept to distant lands you've dreamed of visiting . . . . Intrigue, adventure, romance, and the destiny of many lives will thrill you through each Harlequin Presents novel.

# *Harlequin Presents...*

*The very finest in romantic fiction*

**Get all the latest books before they're sold out!**

As a Harlequin subscriber you actually receive your personal copies of the latest Presents novels immediately after they come off the press, so you're sure of getting all 6 each month.

**Cancel your subscription whenever you wish!**

You don't have to buy any minimum number of books. Whenever you decide to stop your subscription just let us know and we'll cancel all further shipments.

**Your FREE gift includes**

*Sweet Revenge* by **Anne Mather**
*Devil in a Silver Room* by **Violet Winspear**
*Gates of Steel* by **Anne Hampson**
*No Quarter Asked* by **Janet Dailey**